D1458735

J. H. J. Peet
B.Sc., M.Sc., Ph.D., C.Chem., M.R.I.C.

Fundamentals of chemistry
A chemistry textbook for TEC level 2

Longman London and New York

Longman Group Limited London

*Associated companies, branches and representatives
throughout the world*

*Published in the United States of America
by Longman Inc., New York*

First published 1978

ISBN 0 582 41164.5

Library of Congress Cataloging in Publication Data

Peet, James Henry John.
    Fundamentals of chemistry.

        (Longman technician series : Mathematics and
    sciences)
    Includes bibliographical references.
    1. Chemistry.   I. Title.
QD31.2.P43   540   77-26076
ISBN 0-582-41164-5

Set in IBM 10/11 Journal
and printed in Great Britain by Richard Clay (The Chaucer Press) Ltd, Bungay, Suffolk

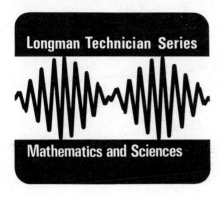

Longman Technician Series

Mathematics and Sciences

General Editor — Mathematics and Sciences
D. R. Browning, B.Sc., F.R.I.C., A.R.T.C.S.
Principal Lecturer and Head of Chemistry,
Bristol Polytechnic

Books to be published in this sector of the series:
Technician mathematics Level 3   **J. O. Bird** and **A. J. C. May**
Mathematics for science technicians Level 2   **J. O. Bird** and **A. J. C. May**
Mathematics for electrical and telecommunications technicians
J. O. Bird and **A. J. C. May**
Physical Science Level 1   **D. R. Browning** and **I. McKenzie Smith**
Engineering Science for Technicians Level 1   **D. R. Browning** and
I. McKenzie Smith

Books already published
Technician mathematics Volume 1   **J. O. Bird** and **A. J. C. May**
Technician mathematics Level 2   **J. O. Bird** and **A. J. C. May**

Contents

Introduction

This textbook is written to meet the requirements of the Technician Education Council level 2 units in Chemistry. It covers the theoretical chemistry necessary for the standard units Chemistry 2 and Laboratory Techniques (Physical Science) 2 issued by the Council. Extra topics have been included to allow for possible local variations in these units and to cover material of value to students following a Biology course.

The SI convention of units and the IUPAC system of nomenclature are followed. Useful references on these approaches are *SI Symbols, Abbreviations and Conventions* (The Council of Technical Examining Bodies) and *Introduction to Chemical Nomenclature* by R. S. Cahn (Butterworths, 4th edn., 1974).

In performing calculations in the SI system, students are advised to convert all quantities (e.g. newtons, pascals, siemens, etc.) to the basic SI units (metres, seconds, kilograms, etc.). This avoids errors arising from the use of mixed terms.

Physical data quoted in the book are taken from the *Nuffield Advanced Science Book of Data* (Longman) and *Tables of Physical and Chemical Constants* by G. W. C. Kaye and T. H. Laby (Longman, 14th edn., 1973).

Each chapter contains a list of recommended experiments, references and films in addition to a selection of questions.

The author acknowledges with gratitude the valued guidance of the editor of this series of publications, Mr David R. Browning.

J. H. J. Peet

Acknowledgements

We are grateful to the following for permission to reproduce copyright material:
City and Guilds of London Institute for data for silver nitrate — bromide conductance measurements from *Chemical Technician* (Part II) First Papers 1973, No. 6; McGraw-Hill Book Company for adaptation of Fig. 17-7 from *General Chemistry* by W. A. Neville. Used with permission of McGraw-Hill Book Co; Mrs. E. McBain for data giving 'Sizes of Colloidal Particles: based on Figs. 12-13 by J. W. McBain from *General College Chemistry* by C. W. Keenan and J. H. Wood (5th Edn.); Oxford University Press and Cornell University Press for Table 3.8 from *The Nature Of The Chemical Bond* by Linus Pauling. Copyright © 1939, 1940 by Cornell University. Used by permission of Cornell University Press. Published in U.K. and Commonwealth by Oxford University Press. Cover photograph by Paul Brierley.

Part 1

The structure of matter

Chapter 1

The structure of the atom

At the beginning of the nineteenth century, the best description of the nature of matter was that based on the work of Dalton. After a careful examination of the experimental results known at that time (1805), he proposed that elements consist of small indivisible particles called atoms. He successfully interpreted a wide range of qualitative and quantitative observations on the basis of this postulate.

Atomic spectra

Two sets of observations in the later years of the nineteenth century formed the basis for a new concept of the atom.

1. When white light is passed through a prism, it produces a spectrum of colours (Fig. 1.1).
2. If the light is passed through hydrogen gas, a series of dark lines occur (Fig. 1.2). These dark lines arise from the absorption of energy. It is found that these energy values are invariable for hydrogen — that is the lines always occur in the same positions — but they are distinct in position, and therefore energy, from those of any other element. Similar absorptions of energy occur in other regions of the spectrum; for example, energy is absorbed from infrared and ultraviolet radiations. The

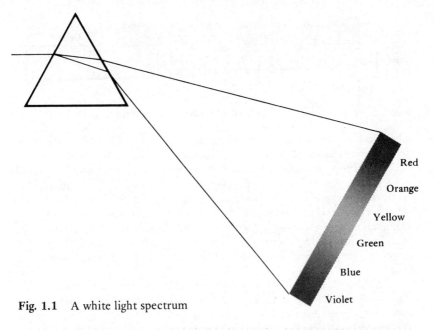

Fig. 1.1 A white light spectrum

infrared, ultraviolet and visible light radiations are a part of the *electromagnetic spectrum*; other regions involve radio waves, microwaves, gamma- and X-radiation (see physics textbooks for full details). The spectra produced for elements such as hydrogen (Fig. 1.2) are known as *atomic spectra*.

Fig. 1.2 Atomic absorption spectrum for hydrogen

A scientific model was required, therefore, to explain why atoms could have the specific properties implied in these experiments.

Radiation

The other significant advance was initiated by Becquerel in 1897. He discovered that certain elements were radioactive, that is they emitted radiation spontaneously. Three types of radiation were identified: α-radiation, β-radiation and γ-radiation. Simultaneously Sir J. J. Thomson observed that the radiation emanating from the cathode of a cathode-ray tube (Fig. 1.3) consisted of negatively charged particles which were called electrons. His work indicated that the electrons were emitted by all gases used to fill the

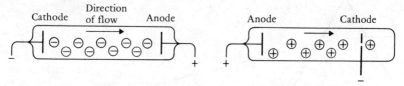

Fig. 1.3   The formation of (*a*) cathode and (*b*) anode rays

tube and had a mass and charge which was independent of the nature of the gas. So, presumably all gases consist, in part at least, of identical electrons. The β-radiation was found to be identical in character with these electrons. γ-radiation was of a similar form to X-radiation but was of higher energy.

α-radiation was found to consist of positively charged helium atoms. The radiation was trapped as a gas above mercury in a closed glass tube. An examination of the atomic spectrum indicated that it was identical with that of helium, which had been identified in the sun's spectrum. The positive charge on the radiation was confirmed by the deflecting effect of a magnetic field.

Goldstein (1886) was able to identify positive radiation in a modified version of the cathode-ray tube. In contrast to the formation of electrons, the positive particles had a mass and charge determined by the nature of the gas. The charge and mass were found, however, to be multiples of that obtained for hydrogen. The experimental evidence suggested that the hydrogen atom possessed one unit of positive charge, called the *proton*, and one unit of negative charge, the *electron*.

Atomic structure

Moseley, in 1914, was able to show that each element had a distinctive number of protons in each of its atoms. This is known as the *atomic number* (see Table 1.1). Atoms have an overall neutral charge, that is the number of protons is equal to the number of electrons, unless: (*a*) the atoms are exposed to a large energy (as in a discharge tube) so causing the loss of an electron; or (*b*) the atom is involved in the formation of an ionic compound (Ch. 3).

Table 1.1   A selection of values of the atomic numbers

Aluminium	13	Gold	79	Magnesium	12
Barium	56	Hydrogen	1	Mercury	80
Calcium	20	Iodine	53	Nitrogen	7
Carbon	6	Iron	26	Oxygen	8
Copper	29	Lead	82	Zinc	30

In 1911, Geiger and Marsden, research students of Lord Rutherford, investigated the effect of high energy α-particles bombarding a gold foil. A small proportion of the particles were deflected from the incident path,

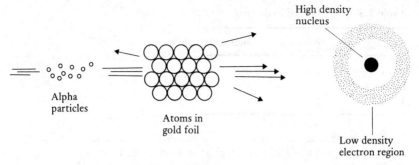

some actually being deflected backwards; the remainder passed straight through the foil. Rutherford is reported as commenting that the backward deflection was so surprising that it was as if someone had fired a 15-inch artillery shell at a piece of tissue paper and it rebounded and hit the gunner. He deduced that the gold atoms must consist of a central, positively charged and dense nucleus, surrounded by a low density region of electrons. In 1932, Chadwick was able to show the existence of *neutrons* as well as protons in the nucleus of atoms. Table 1.2 lists the basic physical properties of these atomic particles. It is observed that the mass of the atom is concentrated in the protons and neutrons with relative masses of 1 atomic mass unit (a.m.u.) each. The number of protons plus neutrons is termed the *mass number*. By convention we represent these values in the form $^{23}_{11}$Na. The lower left integer is the atomic number; the upper left numeral is the mass number, i.e. sodium has an atomic number of 11 and mass number of 23.

Table 1.2 Properties of the fundamental particles

Particle	Charge		Mass	
	Absolute value/C	Relative value	Absolute value/g	Relative value
Electron	-1.60×10^{-19}	-1	9.1×10^{-28}	0
Proton	$+1.60 \times 10^{-19}$	$+1$	1.67×10^{-24}	1
Neutron	0	0	1.67×10^{-24}	1

While Moseley had been able to establish that the atomic number was a characteristic of an element, it was found that the mass number could vary for the atoms of a given element. For example, the element hydrogen is known to have three different types of atom (see Table 1.3). Each type of atom contains one proton (hence atomic number 1), but they have differing numbers of neutrons (0,1 or 2). The mass numbers of the hydrogen atoms can be either 1,2 or 3 (the number of protons plus the number of neutrons). Atoms of an element that are related in this way are known as *isotopes*. It is not normal for isotopes to have different names. (Table 1.3 shows the exception, hydrogen.)

Table 1.3 Isotopes of hydrogen

	Protons	Neutrons
Hydrogen	1	0
Deuterium	1	1
Tritium	1	2

Chlorine has an isotope of atomic number 17, mass number 36. How many protons, neutrons and electrons are present in this atom?

The atomic number gives the number of protons (17). The number of electrons is equal to the number of protons. The number of neutrons is given by the difference between the mass number (equal to the number of protons and neutrons) and the atomic number. So, the number of neutrons is $36 - 17 = 19$.

Naturally-occurring elements are found to be a mixture of several isotopes. The proportion of the isotopes in a sample of an element is remarkably constant and generally independent of the source of the element. In normal chemical reactions (as distinct from 'nuclear chemistry') we do not attempt to separate the isotopes. Therefore, rather than use the mass number of the individual isotopes, chemists use the relative atomic mass (also called the atomic weight) of the element. This is an average value of the mass numbers, allowing for the unequal quantities of the isotopes in the element. For example, neon consists of:

90.5% isotope 20
9.2% isotope 22
0.3% isotope 21

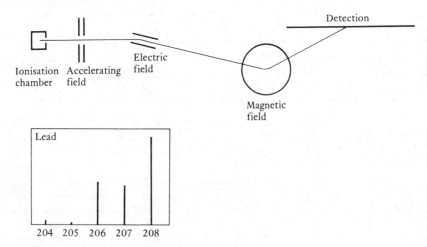

Fig. 1.4 Schematic diagrams of a mass spectrometer and a mass spectrum

The relative atomic mass

$$= \frac{90.5}{100} \times 20 + \frac{9.2}{100} \times 22 + \frac{0.3}{100} \times 21$$

$$= 18.10 \qquad + 2.02 \qquad + 0.06$$

$$= 20.18$$

The composition of an element, in terms of its isotopes, is determined using a mass spectrometer. The element is vaporised in an evacuated chamber and the atoms are ionised by bombardment with electrons. The ions are accelerated in an electric field and then deflected by a combination of electric and magnetic fields. For particles of equal charge, the deflection is proportional to the mass. So, there is a signal in the mass spectrum corresponding to each isotope (Fig. 1.4). Neon, for example, will have three peaks. The intensity of the peaks is dependent on the relative abundance of the isotopes.

Radioactivity

Many isotopes are stable to nuclear change, but some apparently have proportions of protons and neutrons which may cause instability. Potassium has three isotopes, 93.3 per cent ^{39}K, 6.7 per cent ^{41}K and 0.01 per cent ^{40}K. Of these, ^{41}K is unstable and emits β-radiation. Some elements have several isotopes all of which are radioactive; for example, uranium has the isotopes 233, 234, 235, 236, 238 and 239 all of which are radioactive.

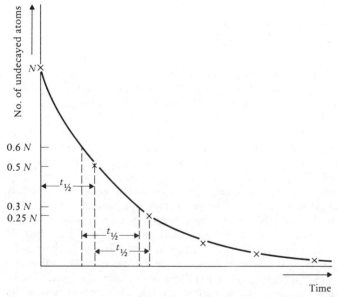

Fig. 1.5 Rate of decay of a radioactive element

In spite of the inherent instability of these isotopes, the decay process is random. It is not possible to predict when a specific atom will disintegrate, but it is found that *on average* each isotope has a particular rate of decay. The decay curve (Fig. 1.5) is exponential in form and obeys a law of the mathematical form

$$N_t = N_0 \cdot e^{-\lambda \cdot t}$$

where N_0 and N_t are the numbers of radioactive atoms existing initially and after a time t secs respectively, λ being a constant known as the 'decay constant'. An interesting feature of this property is that there is associated with each radioactive isotope a *half-life* $(t_{1/2})$. The half-life is the time taken for the number of radioactive atoms to reduce to one-half of its initial number. This time is independent of the initial number of atoms. For example, in Fig. 1.5, the half-life is the time taken for the number of active atoms to reduce from N to $0.5\,N$, or from $0.5\,N$ to $0.25\,N$, or from $0.6\,N$ to $0.3\,N$, and so on. Table 1.4 lists a selection of isotopes and their half-lives. It has been generally assumed that the half-life of an isotope is constant, but recent research has shown that it is affected by its chemical and physical environments.

Table 1.4   Some common isotopes and their half-lives

^{14}C	5 570 y*
^{40}K	1.3×10^9 y
^{131}I	8.06 d
^{238}U	4.5×10^9 y

(*other values have been recommended, see page 11)

At first consideration it might appear to be a nuisance to have elements that disintegrate while they are being used. However, radioactivity has proved to be a useful tool in chemistry and biology as well as in engineering and similar fields. The value of radioactivity lies in its sensitivity to detection. 1 g of ^{24}Na forms 3×10^{17} β-particles per second. Standard detecting equipment, such as the Geiger counter, can detect and record one particle a second with ease. As a result it is not impossible with reasonable equipment to analyse to an accuracy of 10^{-12} g.

Radioisotopes can also be used as tracers since the active isotopes have the same chemical and physical properties as the stable isotopes. 'Tracers' are atoms that can be used to follow the progress of another substance in a mechanical or chemical system. They must have properties similar to those of the substance under investigation. The effect is that, whereas the non-radioactive substance may be difficult to follow in the system, the radioactive substance can easily be detected and so followed. For example, tracers can be used to indicate the path of the carbon dioxide absorbed by a plant in photosynthesis. The chemicals produced by the plant can be isolated after various times, analysed and examined for the presence of radioactive carbon.

Tracers can also be used quantitatively. The proportion of the radioactive isotope to the inactive isotope in the starting material and the proportion in the final product is the same. If carbon dioxide is mixed with the radioactive gas ($^{14}CO_2$), it is possible to determine the percentage of the gas used in photosynthesis. For example, if the radioactive gas records a count rate of 1 000 counts per minute (that is 1 000 particles are detected by the counter in a minute), but an isolated sugar gives a count rate of only 200 counts per minute, it implies that only 20 per cent of all the carbon dioxide (active and inactive) has been converted to the sugar.

It is difficult to prove that a dynamic equilibrium exists in a saturated solution, that is the solid is deposited from solution at the same rate as solid is dissolved into solution. If lead iodide containing a trace of radioactive iodine(^{131}I) ion is added to a saturated solution of lead iodide, it is found that the ^{131}I is distributed between the two phases, indicating an interchange of species.

Similar techniques can be used in medical diagnosis. Small doses of radioactive iodine (^{131}I) can be fed to a patient to record the uptake of iodine by the thyroid gland or to record the size of the active part of the gland, so detecting possible abnormalities.

If a supply of radioactive calcium (^{45}Ca) is introduced into the patient's diet and it tends to become located at a specific area of the bone structure, it suggests a bone cancer at this point. This is because, due to an increase in the rate of cell division in the malignancy, the cancerous cells have a greater rate of uptake of calcium than do the non-malignant bone cells.

Pernicious anaemia can be effectively diagnosed using vitamin B_{12} incorporating one of the active cobalt isotopes. This blood deficiency occurs when the body is unable to absorb vitamin B_{12} into the blood stream. Since the amount of the vitamin in the diet is small, making its detection difficult, its absorption is followed by the use of the vitamin containing the ^{60}Co isotope. In a healthy person, over 60 per cent of the activity can be detected in the blood within a few hours. A patient suffering from pernicious anaemia absorbs less than 10 per cent.

More intensive doses of radiation are lethal to living organisms and so can be used for sterilisation of instruments or destruction of cancerous cells. Radioactive materials must be treated with care since, aside from the normal chemical toxicity, they are liable to cause a number of complaints from radiation sickness to cancers and death.

If the rate of decay of an isotope is constant, then a measure of the concentration of the decay products is theoretically a means of determining the age of the material under investigation. A number of such 'radioactive clocks' have been suggested. Rocks containing uranium-238 can be dated by the amount of lead-206 present as a result of the decay of ^{238}U. The uranium-238 decays into this isotope of lead in a series of steps:

$$^{238}_{92}U \xrightarrow{\alpha\text{-decay}} {}^{234}_{90}Th \xrightarrow{\beta} {}^{234}_{91}Pa \xrightarrow{\beta} {}^{234}_{92}U \xrightarrow{\alpha} {}^{230}_{90}Th \xrightarrow{\alpha}$$

$$\overset{226}{\underset{88}{}}\text{Ra} \xrightarrow{\ a\ } \overset{222}{\underset{86}{}}\text{Rn} \xrightarrow{\ a\ } \overset{218}{\underset{84}{}}\text{Po} \xrightarrow{\ a\ } \overset{214}{\underset{82}{}}\text{Pb} \xrightarrow{\ \beta\ } \overset{214}{\underset{83}{}}\text{Bi} \xrightarrow{\ a\ }$$

$$\overset{210}{\underset{81}{}}\text{Tl} \xrightarrow{\ \beta\ } \overset{210}{\underset{82}{}}\text{Pb} \xrightarrow{\ \beta\ } \overset{210}{\underset{83}{}}\text{Bi} \xrightarrow{\ a\ } \overset{206}{\underset{81}{}}\text{Tl} \xrightarrow{\ \beta\ } \overset{206}{\underset{82}{}}\text{Pb (stable)}$$

The amount of lead-206, which is non-radioactive, in the rock is controlled in part by the age of the rock, that is the length of time over which the uranium-238 has been decaying.

Similarly, the decay of ^{40}K (by γ-radiation) gives argon gas which is trapped in the rocks. A measurement of the amount of argon-40 in the rock sample is the basis for dating the rock. Rubidium-87 decays into strontium-87 by β-decay to give an alternative dating system. The half-line has been estimated as 49.9×10^9 years. If the amount of ^{87}Sr is determined, it is possible to calculate the fraction of ^{87}Rb that has decayed. From a knowledge of the half-life, the age of the rock can be computed. (A typical calculation of an age is described below.)

Living materials contain carbon. Carbon-14 occurs naturally due to the irradiation of atmospheric nitrogen with cosmic neutrons.

$$^{14}_{7}\text{N} + ^{1}_{0}\text{n} \rightarrow ^{14}_{6}\text{C} + ^{1}_{1}\text{p}$$

The age of a dead organic substance is estimated from the ratio of ^{14}C to ^{12}C on the assumption that the ratio at death was equal to the present-day atmospheric value. The ratio of ^{14}C to ^{12}C after death decreases due to the decay of the carbon-14. From a knowledge of the rate of decay of ^{14}C, it is possible to determine the length of time that has passed since the object died.

An example of the method of estimating the age of an object is given in the following analytical results. A fragment of a Viking ship is found to have an activity of 10.66 counts per minute (that is the amount of radiation detected by a suitable instrument). A similar piece of modern wood has a count rate of 12.24 cpm. The decay curve for a piece of wood of this size is as shown in Fig. 1.6.

As time passes (horizontal axis) the activity decreases. After 5 570 y, the half-life of carbon-14, the activity will be half that in the initial sample. An activity of 10.66 cpm corresponds to an age of 1 100 years.

Unfortunately these techniques are less reliable than is often assumed. There are serious discrepancies between the techniques (for example, radio-carbon dating is generally quoted as giving dates of the order of tens of thousands of years; the other techniques give tens of millions of years or more). A number of potential sources of error are apparent; for example:

(a) a loss of gas (argon) from the rocks by diffusion;

(b) a loss of isotopes due to leaching (removal of minerals by solution), for example, up to 40 per cent of the uranium in some ores can be removed by the action of a weak acid;

(c) the assumption that, for example, no lead-210 was present originally;

(d) the assumption that there was no contamination of the sample with daughter products (i.e. the products of decay) in historical times; for

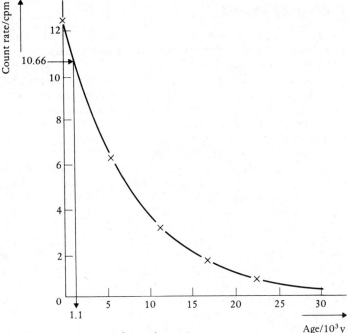

Fig. 1.6   Decay curve for carbon-14

example, the amount of carbon-14 in the atmosphere has approximately doubled in the last decade or two as a result of nuclear bomb testing;

(e) the assumption that there has been no fluctuation in the rate of production of carbon-14, though this too is improbable as variations in the earth's magnetic fields would have affected cosmic bombardment of the atmosphere.

These factors will tend to reduce the apparent ages determined by these methods. Probably the best that can be claimed at present is that they give estimates of relative ages. We can only assign dates with complete confidence when we have an independent means of correlation. For example, many carbon-14 dates have been cross-checked with known historical dates, particularly of Egyptian archives. It has been found that there is a wide discrepancy between ^{14}C dates and those obtained by tree-ring measurements, the deviations being up to 700 years. Results such as these have led scientists to redetermine the half-life values and re-examine their theories. The half-life of carbon has been amended to 5 730 y (from 5 570 y) in order to improve these inconsistencies, though errors still arise. A similar problem arises in the potassium-argon dating of recent volcanic rocks. For example, tests have been made on rocks at Hualalai, Hawaii which are known to have been formed in 1800–1801. This dating technique gives values of 1 to 2 thousand million years! Clearly some of the argon has been trapped from other sources. Obviously data for which no independent check is available must be used with caution.

Atomic energy levels

It was noted earlier in the chapter that, in an atomic spectrum, certain energies are absorbed (see Fig. 1.2). Each element has its own set of absorption energies. Bohr, a Danish scientist, suggested that this could be explained on the assumption that the electrons are moving outside of the nucleus, but are attracted by it. (The details of his model are not discussed here in view of the fact that we now interpret the experimental data differently in terms of the detail.) Of course, if the nucleus experiences a change in the number of protons, the forces of attraction on the electrons also change and consequently the energies absorbed by the atoms differ.

The hydrogen atom possesses one electron. The energy possessed by this electron is -21.74×10^{-19} J. The minus sign is used by convention to indicate that, when the electron is placed in the atom, energy is released. Energy losses are always given a negative sign. When hydrogen atoms are irradiated, it is found that the electron will absorb the energies: 16.340×10^{-19} J; 19.367×10^{-19} J; 20.426×10^{-19} J, etc. These are the values indicated by the dark lines in Fig. 1.2. These changes can be illustrated in an energy level diagram (Fig. 1.7(a)). As shown in the figure, each level is designated by a value, n. This value is known as the *principal quantum number*. Each of the values in this series of lines represents an absorption in the ultraviolet region. The largest value of absorbed energy in this atom is 21.74×10^{-19} J. This energy is known as the ionisation energy and is the energy required to strip an atom of an electron. If the electron is 'excited' from the $n = 1$ level to the $n = 2$ level, it is then able to absorb a new series of energy values: 3.027×10^{-19} J; 4.086×10^{-19} J; 4.577×10^{-19} J, etc. (Fig. 1.7(b)). These lines represent the changes from $n = 2$ to higher levels ($2 \to 3$; $2 \to 4$; $2 \to 5$, etc.). These values correspond to the visible region of the spectrum.

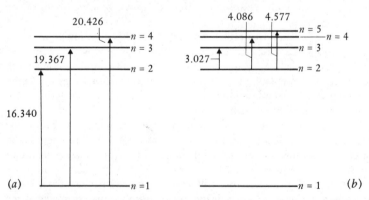

Fig. 1.7(a) and (b)   Energy level diagram for hydrogen ($J/10^{-19}$)

Other series exist and are based on the absorptions from higher levels ($n = 3$, $n = 4$, etc.). Each of these series was discovered by a different scientist and the series are known by the names of their discoverers: the Lyman series

(from the lowest level, $n = 1$), Balmer series (from $n = 2$ level), Paschen
($n = 3$), Brackett ($n = 4$) and Pfund ($n = 5$) series.

In this discussion reference has been made to the absorption of energy by hydrogen atoms causing the formation of black lines in the spectrum. It is possible to give the hydrogen atom energy from sources other than electro-magnetic radiation (see page 3). For example, electrical energy can excite the electron in the hydrogen atom. However, the nucleus is exerting an attractive force on the electron; this causes the electron to be drawn as close to the nucleus as possible. The position actually occupied will be a balance between this attractive force and forces of opposite effect arising, for example, from the motion of the electron. If the only force acting on the electron were that of the nucleus, then the electron would be drawn into the nucleus.

When the electron is excited to the $n = 3$ level, then the electron can drop to either the $n = 2$ or $n = 1$ levels (Fig. 1.8). In doing this, energy is released; 3.027×10^{-19} J, and 19.367×10^{-19} J in this particular example. As a result, a spectrum of sharp coloured lines is formed (Fig. 1.9). This is an *emission spectrum*.

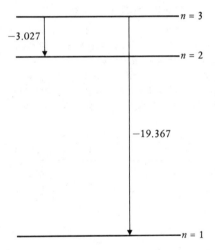

Fig. 1.8   Emission of energy in hydrogen (J/10^{-19})

The atomic spectra vary with the element examined, indicating that the energy levels are dependent on the nuclear charge. Construction of energy level diagrams for elements other than hydrogen shows that the energy levels

Red   Blue   Violet Violet

Fig. 1.9   Emission spectrum of hydrogen

14

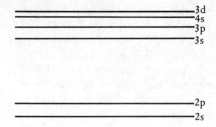

Fig. 1.10   Energy level diagram for elements other than hydrogen

are more complex than those for hydrogen (cf. Fig. 1.7 and 1.10). For most values of *n*, there are several sub-levels (Fig. 1.10). These sub-levels are given the labels s, p and d, which are known as the *azimuthal quantum numbers*. (The choice of these letters was determined from an examination of spectral lines related to these states and they were classified as *s*harp, *p*rincipal and *d*iffuse lines.) In the case of hydrogen, the energy of these sub-levels is coincident.

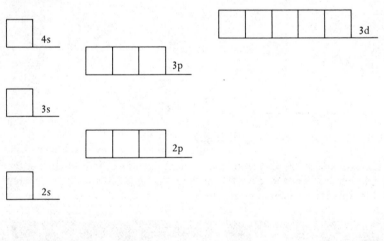

Fig. 1.11   Orbital energy levels

It is found that the sub-levels contain electrons with different spatial orientations. All the s electrons have a spherical distribution about the nucleus. On the other hand, the p electrons (i.e. those in the 2p, 3p, 4p levels etc.) have three possible orientations — at right angles to each other. The d sub-levels have five possible orientations of the electrons. We call these individual orientations, *orbitals*. The orbitals are often represented by a box notation (Fig. 1.11). These orbitals are differentiated by the application of a magnetic field; this causes a splitting of the lines of an atomic spectrum. The different orbitals of the same energy are described by the *magnetic quantum number*. So, for the 2p level, the subscripts x, y and z represent this quantum number. It is found that only two electrons can occupy a single orbital. Each electron spins about its axis creating a magnetic field (electric currents give magnetic fields). So the two electrons must have opposite spins or else they would repel each other, due to the similar electric magnetic fields. When two electrons of opposite spin occupy an orbital they are said to be paired. The *spin quantum number* indicates the direction of spin. These are represented thus in our box convention:

Let us consider the element sodium. One of its isotopes has a mass number of 23 and an atomic number 11. How many protons, neutrons and electrons are present in the atom?

The atomic number (11) indicates the number of protons (11). Since the atom has an overall neutral charge, the number of protons must equal the number of electrons. The mass number specifies the number of nuclear particles (protons plus neutrons), so there are $23 - 11 = 12$ neutrons. We know that the 11 electrons can occupy several energy states (Fig. 1.10). The 'Aufbau principle' (from the German for 'construction') gives a set of empirical rules to enable us to specify the arrangement of electrons in a system.

(*a*) An electron will always occupy the lowest available energy level. The order of availability of the levels for an atom is as shown in Fig. 1.11:

1s, 2s, 2p, 3s, 3p, 4s, 3d, 4p, 5s, etc.

(*b*) If two or more orbitals are of the same energy, then each orbital will contain one electron before any of the other orbitals receives a second one (Hund's rule). For example, the 2p level consists of the orbitals $2p_x$, $2p_y$ and $2p_z$. If there are two electrons to occupy these orbitals, then, according to Hund's Rule, one electron will occupy $2p_x$ and one will occupy $2p_y$, rather than two in $2p_x$. (The electrons could equally well be distributed between $2p_x$ and $2p_z$ or between $2p_y$ and $2p_z$.)

$2p_x$ $2p_y$ $2p_z$

(*c*) No two electrons can have the same set of four quantum numbers in an atom (Pauli's exclusion principle). So, if two electrons must occupy the $2p_x$ orbital (the same principal, azimuthal and magnetic quantum numbers) they will have different spin quantum numbers.

16

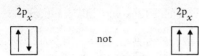

$2p_x$ not $2p_x$

Applying these rules to the sodium isotope described above ($^{23}_{11}$Na), we find the structure is as shown in Fig. 1.12.

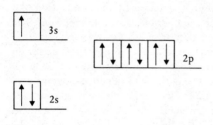

Fig. 1.12 Electronic structure of sodium

Determine the structure of iron, atomic number 26.

An atomic number of 26 indicates the presence of 26 protons and so of 26 electrons. Applying the Aufbau principle you should obtain the structure illustrated in Fig. 1.13. This method of writing structures consumes a lot of

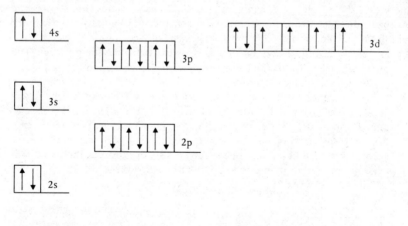

Fig. 1.13 Electronic structure of iron

Atomic number	Element	Electronic structure
1	Hydrogen	$1s^1$
2	Helium	$1s^2$
3	Lithium	$1s^2 2s^1$
4	Beryllium	$1s^2 2s^2$
5	Boron	$1s^2 2s^2 2p^1$
6	Carbon	$1s^2 2s^2 2p^2$
7	Nitrogen	$1s^2 2s^2 2p^3$
8	Oxygen	$1s^2 2s^2 2p^4$
9	Fluorine	$1s^2 2s^2 2p^5$
10	Neon	$1s^2 2s^2 2p^6$
11	Sodium	$1s^2 2s^2 2p^6 3s^1$
12	Magnesium	$1s^2 2s^2 2p^6 3s^2$
13	Aluminium	$1s^2 2s^2 2p^6 3s^2 3p^1$
14	Silicon	$1s^2 2s^2 2p^6 3s^2 3p^2$
15	Phosphorus	$1s^2 2s^2 2p^6 3s^2 3p^3$
16	Sulphur	$1s^2 2s^2 2p^6 3s^2 3p^4$
17	Chlorine	$1s^2 2s^2 2p^6 3s^2 3p^5$
18	Argon	$1s^2 2s^2 2p^6 3s^2 3p^6$
19	Potassium	$1s^2 2s^2 2p^6 3s^2 3p^6 4s^1$
20	Calcium	$1s^2 2s^2 2p^6 3s^2 3p^6 4s^2$

space. A more compact arrangement is $1s^2\ 2s^2\ 2p^6\ 3s^8\ 3p^6\ 4s^2\ 3d^6$. If it is desirable to emphasise the internal arrangement of the 3d electrons, then these can be written out separately.

Table 1.5 lists the electronic configurations of the twenty elements with atomic numbers 1 to 20.

We are now able to describe the electronic arrangement of the atoms in terms of the energy states. In order to determine the way in which atoms bond together (Ch. 2) we need to know the position of the electrons. We see the position of ordinary objects because they are able to reflect visible light. Smaller particles such as atoms, nuclei and electrons have to be detected by the reflection of radiation of shorter wavelength and so of higher energy. Unfortunately, because of the small mass of the electron, the energy of the radiation used to locate an electron gives it a 'kick' so that it is impossible to detect with any certainty the position of the electron. This is the effect described in 'Heisenberg's uncertainty principle'. This principle states that it is impossible to determine precisely both the position and the momentum of a particle, such as an electron. The more precisely its velocity is known (and so its momentum), the less accurately its position can be determined.

The best that it is possible to determine is the most probable position of the electron. It is now customary to describe the electron position in terms of an electron density or probability diagram. For an electron in a 1s orbital we

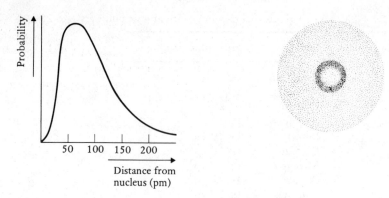

Fig. 1.14   Electron probability diagrams for the 1s electron

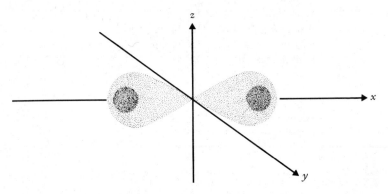

Fig. 1.15   Electron probability diagrams for a $2p_x$ electron

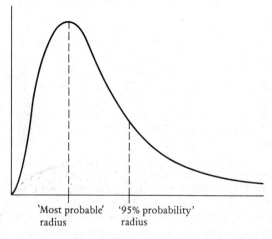

'Most probable'   '95% probability'
radius   radius

Fig. 1.16   Alternative representations of atomic radii

find that the probability of finding an electron is equal in all directions (that   19
is it has a spherical symmetry). In Fig. 1.14 the way the electron probability
varies with the distance from the nucleus is shown together with the electron
density plot (in two dimensions) for this electron. The more dense the
shading, the greater the probability of an electron occupying that position.

Similar probability diagrams can be drawn for other orbitals. Figure 1.15
illustrates the form for $2p_x$.

Having discussed the nature of the atom, we can now consider the
question, how big is an atom? The nucleus is estimated to have a diameter of
the order of 10^{-15} m. The most probable position of an electron gives a
diameter of the order of 10^{-10} m. But consider what this represents in our
earlier diagram (Fig. 1.14). Clearly there is a significant electron density
beyond this point. It is, therefore, more normal to quote the size of an atom
as that distance which involves 95 per cent of the electron density (Fig. 1.16).

Summary

At the conclusion of this chapter, you should be able to:

1. state that the presence of dark lines in a spectrum is due to the
   absorption of energy by atoms;
2. account for the production of an emission spectrum;
3. describe the nature of α-, β- and γ-radiation;
4. state the relationship between the nuclear structure and the atomic and
   mass numbers;
5. determine the electronic structure given the atomic number;
6. state what is meant by an isotope;
7. calculate the relative atomic mass given the isotopic composition;
8. describe the construction and use of a mass spectrometer;
9. state what is meant by radioactivity;
10. define the half-life of a radioactive isotope;
11. explain how radioisotopes are used in analytical chemistry and in medical
    diagnosis and treatment;
12. state the principle underlying the use of radioactive decay as a dating
    process and the errors which affect such dating processes;
13. draw an atomic energy level diagram and relate it to the atomic spectra;
14. describe the nature of the four quantum numbers;
15. quote and apply the rules of the Aufbau principle;
16. write the electronic structure of an element up to atomic number 20
    given its atomic number;
17. state Heisenberg's uncertainty principle;
18. comment on the significance of an electron's position and an atom's size
    with respect to the electron probability diagram.

Experiments

1. Examine the emission spectrum of some elements using a pocket direct vision spectroscope.
2. Flame test the s-block metals.
3. Radioactivity experiments — a variety of experiments are available based on common potassium, uranium and thorium salts (e.g. half-life of Rn, Pa, K, Pb; growth curve of Pa; solubility of K, Pb and Tl salts; dating using uranium; radiometric analysis using Th, Pb; use of tracers in plants, e.g. Tl, etc.).

References

Atomic energy levels — hydrogen and sodium; K. S. Tetlow, *Sch. Sci. Rev.*, 1971, **53**, 323—30.
Atomic analysis in flames; T. S. West, *Endeavour*, 1967, **26**, 44—9.
Stereo plots of hydrogen-like electron densities; D. T. Cromer, *J. Chem. Educ.*, 1968, **45**, 626—32.
Radioactivity — an assortment of literature is available from The Isotope Information Bureau, U.K.A.E.A., London.
Radioisotope Experiments in Physics, Chemistry and Biology; J. B. Dance (Hutchinson, 2nd edn., 1973).
Mass spectrometry, Part 1. The spectrometer; R. I. Reed and D. H. Robertson, *Chemistry*, 1976, **42**, 7—11.

Films

The hydrogen atom, as viewed by quantum mechanics (CHEM Study).
Radioactivity (McGraw-Hill).
Atomic energy explained (Commonwealth Relations Office).
Radiochemistry for schools (I.C.I.).
Analysis by mass (A.E.I. Ltd.).
Conquest of the atom (Mullard Ltd.).

Filmloops

The spectrum of the hydrogen atom (Longman).
Evidence for excitation (Longman).
Applications of mass spectrometry (Nuffield).

Questions

1. Yellow street lights contain sodium vapour. From your knowledge of the

electronic structure of sodium and the formation of emission spectra,
how do you account for the yellow colour?

2. A sample of chlorine is found to contain the isotopes $^{35}_{17}$ Cl and $^{37}_{17}$ Cl (75 per cent and 25 per cent respectively). What is meant by the term 'isotope'? Describe the atomic structure of each isotope. What would be the relative atomic mass of the mixture?

3. Boron consists of two isotopes; 18.83 per cent $^{10}_{5}$B and 81.17 per cent $^{11}_{5}$B. Determine the relative atomic mass.

4. The following readings were obtained in an experiment on a radioactive solution. Determine the half-life of the isotope present in the solution.

Time/sec	10	40	70	100	150	180	200	250	300
Count rate/cps	1075	860	681	552	378	301	260	177	125

5. Find out as many applications of radioactivity in industry and science as you can.

6. Describe the method by which old rocks can be dated using the decay of radioactive isotopes.

7. Obtain information about recently formed volcanic islands (e.g. Surtsey). What have been the results of radioactive dating of these?

8. Write down the electronic structure of $_5$B, $_9$F, $_{12}$Mg, $_{15}$P and $_{20}$Ca.

9. Describe the difference between α-, β- and γ-radiation.

10. What do you understand by the term 'size of an atom'?

Chapter 2

The structure of a molecule

A molecule is formed when two or more atoms are held together by substantial forces. As will be apparent in Chapter 4, there are relatively weak forces between atoms or molecules (intermolecular forces) but these are usually ruptured in such processes as fusion and solution. Their physical nature is also fundamentally different from the forces holding atoms together in a molecule.

Covalent bonding

The atoms are held together by a pair of electrons which are attracted by the nuclei of both atoms. We have seen in Chapter 1 that electrons occupy positions of minimum energy with respect to an atomic nucleus.

For the most stable bonding the electrons occupy the minimum energy positions of both atoms. This results in an overlap of the orbitals (Fig. 2.1). Pauli's principle is still applicable.

Consider two hydrogen atoms (labelled H_a and H_b for clarity). Each atom has the electronic configuration $1s^1$. For efficient bonding the electron

H_a ⬆ H_b ⬇

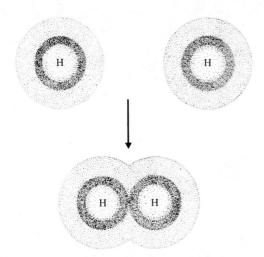

Fig. 2.1 The interaction of 1s orbitals on hydrogen atoms to form the hydrogen molecule

on H_a must also occupy the 1s orbital of H_b. This it can do if, and only if, H_b can accept an electron of that particular spin into its orbital. H_b contains an electron of spin designated ↓ so it can accept an electron of the opposite spin ↑ into this same orbital. This happens if atom H_a moves closer to H_b, so that the electron in H_a coincides with the minimum energy (or maximum probability) position of H_b.

H_a ⟦↑ ↓⟧ H_b

In contrast, a hydrogen atom cannot bond to a helium atom because the helium orbital is fully occupied and so cannot contain the hydrogen atom's electron

H ⟦↑⟧ ⟦↓ ↑⟧ He

Consider hydrogen fluoride, HF. From an examination of the electronic

H ⟦↓⟧ F ⟦↑ ↓⟧ ⟦↑ ↓⟧ ⟦↑ ↓ ↑ ↓ ↑⟧

configurations of the two atoms, it is apparent that bonding can only occur by the sharing of the 1s electron on hydrogen and the unpaired 2p electron on fluorine (Fig. 2.2).

This form of bonding by the sharing of a pair of electrons is described as *covalency*. Before proceeding further it would be useful to describe the formation of the covalent bond in chlorine, Cl_2.

24

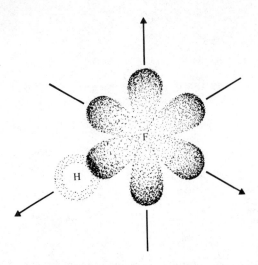

Fig. 2.2 The interaction of the hydrogen 1s and fluorine 2p orbitals to form HF

Chlorine has five electrons in the 3p energy state. If the two chlorine atoms approach so that the half-filled orbitals can overlap, then pairing can occur:

$3p_z$

Cl_a | ↑ ↓ | Cl_b

The structure of ammonia, NH_3, can be explained in a similar manner. There are three unpaired electrons on the nitrogen.

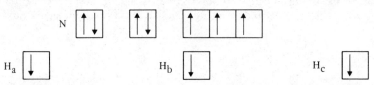

Each of these can pair with an unpaired hydrogen electron (Fig. 2.3).

An examination of Fig. 2.3 shows the covalent bonds to be at right angles, along the three axes. However, the experimentally determined angle in ammonia is $107.3°$.

In order to explain situations such as this, Sidgwick and Powell proposed the 'valence shell electron pair repulsion theory'. In the outer region of the nitrogen atom there are four pairs of electrons — a non-bonding pair nominally in the 2s orbital and three bonding pairs in the 2p orbitals. This outer region of electrons, the region containing the electrons involved in bonding, is known as the *valence shell*. These electron pairs repel each other and the electrons move to positions which minimise the repulsion. The largest angle of orientation of these electron pairs with respect to each other is the

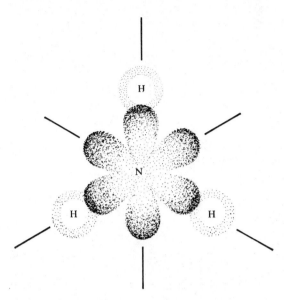

Fig. 2.3 The interaction of nitrogen and hydrogen orbitals to form ammonia

tetrahedral distribution, 109.5°. The new probability diagrams for this tetra-hedral distribution are shown in Fig. 2.4. These orbitals, formed from an s orbital and three p orbitals, are described as *sp₃ hybrid orbitals*. This process, called *hybridisation,* means that one s orbital and three p orbitals are mixed to produce the new hybrid orbital type sp₃. (This is analagous to the concept of hybridisation in the production of new varieties of flowers, for example.)

The discrepancy between the tetrahedral angle (109.5°) and the H—N—H angle (107.3°) is explained by Sidgwick and Powell as being the result of non-bonding pairs exerting a greater repulsion than bonding pairs. So, the bonding electron pairs approach each other more closely to offset this greater repulsion. The resulting molecular shape for ammonia is pyramidal (Fig. 2.5).

Similar reasoning will show that the bond angle in water is of the same order, 104.5°.

Boron forms trivalent compounds (that is compounds with three bonds) such as BCl_3. Consider the electronic structures of the elements. The boron atom has only one unpaired electron. In order to explain the three bonds, it is postulated that the boron receives energy during the reaction to promote one

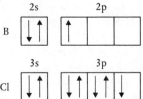

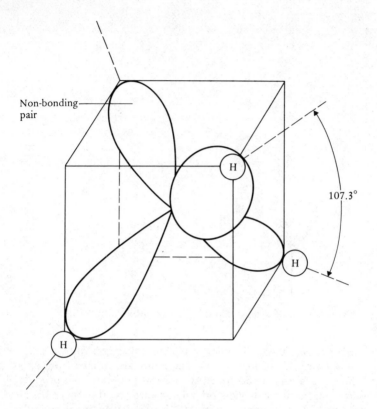

Non-bonding pair

H

H

H

107.3°

Fig. 2.4 The tetrahedral distribution of valence electron pairs in ammonia

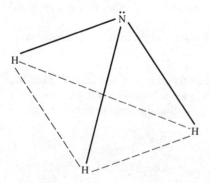

N̈

H

H

H

Fig. 2.5 Pyramidal arrangement of the atoms in ammonia

2s electron to a 2p orbital. Now each of the unpaired electrons can pair with
an unpaired Cl (2p) electron to give three bonding pairs. Applying the

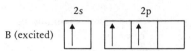

Sidgwick—Powell theory, the three pairs will distribute themselves to give as
large a bond angle as possible. This results in a trigonal planar distribution of
the electron pairs, $120°$ (Fig. 2.6). This arrangement is described as sp_2
hybridisation. So, the formation of sp_2 hybrids involves excitation of a 2s
electron and rearrangement of the orbitals.

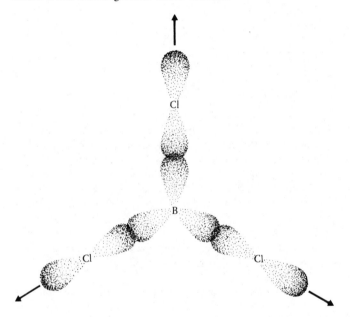

Fig. 2.6 The trigonal planar arrangement of boron(III) chloride

The same process of hybridisation is applied to carbon compounds.
Carbon, with a $2s^2 2p^2$ structure, has two unpaired electrons. In compounds
such as CH_4 and CCl_4 the carbon requires four unpaired electrons. This can be
achieved by promoting an electron from 2s to 2p.

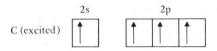

After bonding, the four pairs of electrons are arranged to give a tetrahedral
distribution of the bonds.

Coordinate bonding

It has been shown that boron(III) chloride is a trigonal planar molecule (three bonding pairs of electrons) and ammonia is pyramidal (three bonding pairs and one non-bonding pair). The boron halides combine with ammonia to form an adduct such as $BCl_3 \cdot NH_3$. A bond is formed between the boron and nitrogen. Consider the electronic structure of these elements in their respective compounds.

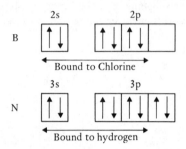

A covalent bond can be formed if the nitrogen non-bonding 3p orbital (with two electrons) overlaps with the empty boron 2p orbital. The resulting bond is indistinguishable from those previously described (even though the electron pair originated from one atom rather than two). It is important to recall our description of a covalent bond. The bond is formed by a pair of electrons, of opposite spin, occupying a region of minimum energy between two nuclei. It is not necessary to specify their origin. However, it is sometimes convenient to refer to this bond, in which one atom donates both electrons, by a distinctive name. When this is desirable, we describe it as a *dative* or *coordinate* bond. Examine the electronic structure of this adduct. What shape would you predict for this molecule?

Each atom has four bonding pairs of electrons; the boron has three to chlorine and one to nitrogen, and the nitrogen has three to hydrogen and one to boron. Therefore, each atom has a tetrahedral stereochemistry (Fig. 2.7).

Fig. 2.7 The tetrahedral configuration of boron and nitrogen in the adduct $BCl_3 \cdot NH_3$

The reaction between ammonia and hydrogen ions to form ammonium ions can be explained on the same principle. The hydrogen ion, H^+, has an empty 1s orbital and readily attracts electrons into this orbital. Why? The non-bonding pair on nitrogen can be donated into this orbital by forming a covalent bond. The presence of four bonding pairs on the nitrogen gives the ammonium ion a tetrahedral arrangement.

The reaction of ammonia with boron(III) chloride and with hydrogen ions forms the basis for an alternative definition of an acid. (Reminder: an acid is a substance that produces hydrogen ions in aqueous solution.) Lewis has suggested that acids can be described as substances that accept a pair of electrons.

This definition of so-called Lewis acids is particularly useful in organic chemistry in which hydrogen ions may not be available. Organic reactions usually involve covalent reactants and solvents which do not facilitate the formation of ions (see page 209). Lewis's definition extends the acid—base concept to these covalent systems. The hydrogen ion is an acid because it accepts a pair of electrons in the above example from ammonia. Similarly, boron(III) chloride is an acid because it accepts the non-bonding pair of electrons from ammonia.

In aqueous solutions, the water molecule (involving two bonding and two non-bonding pairs of electrons) forms a dative bond with hydrogen ions. If one water molecule (H_2O) and one hydrogen ion (H^+) combine in this way, what is the shape of the resulting ion (H_3O^+)? This ion is always formed by hydrogen ions in aqueous solution.

Oxygen has the structure $1s^2\ 2s^2\ 2p_x{}^2\ 2p_y{}^1\ 2p_z{}^1$. Two hydrogen atoms can combine with two unpaired electrons; the hydrogen ion with its empty 1s orbital can interact with the non-bonding $2p_x$ pair of electrons. The molecule

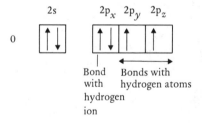

forms sp3 hybrid orbitals. The shape of the molecule is the same as that for the ammonia molecule (Fig. 2.5) with three bonding pairs and one non-bonding pair of electrons.

A Lewis base is a molecule that donates a pair of electrons. So, in these examples, ammonia and water are Lewis bases. Consider the general neutralisation reaction:

$$H^+ + OH^- \rightarrow H_2O$$

The hydroxide ion (three non-bonding pairs, one bonding pair of electrons) forms a dative bond with the hydrogen ion so forming water. The structure of the hydroxide ion can be explained as follows. One of the unpaired 2p electrons of oxygen is paired with the 1s electron of hydrogen. The other unpaired electron is paired by the extra electron received in ion formation. (A preliminary knowledge of ion formation is assumed in this course; a more detailed discussion is included in Ch. 3.)

In these covalent bonds the electron pair lies in between the nuclei and along the internuclear axis. These bonds are named 'sigma bonds' (σ-bonds).

A large number of compounds involve multiple bonds between atoms. Consider, for example, the oxygen molecule, O_2. The electronic configurations of the oxygen atoms are:

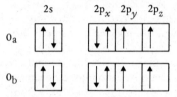

If the oxygen atoms approach along the axis y, the 2p(y) orbitals can interact end-on and form a σ-bond (Fig. 2.8). The 2p(z) orbitals are also half-filled, but an end-on overlap is not possible, because, as the figure shows, they are parallel to each other and perpendicular to the line of approach of

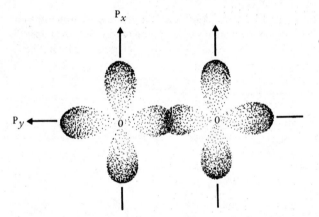

Fig. 2.8 The formation of the σ-covalent bond of oxygen

the atoms. There is a low probability of the electrons interacting but it would not constitute a significant bond. Better interaction would result if the σ-bond length were shortened (Fig. 2.9). In structures like the above the nuclei move closer together to decrease the internuclear distance and strengthen the interaction between the 2p(y) orbitals. The orbital overlap is not along the line joining the two nuclei but parallel to it, in the direction of the z axis. Bonds of this type (i.e. those parallel to the internuclear axis) are described as π-bonds (pi bonds). Because the overlap does not correspond to the position of maximum probability the bond is not so strong as a σ-bond. Less energy is required to rupture this bond.

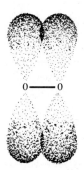

O——O

Fig. 2.9 Formation of the π-bond of oxygen

The energy required to break a chemical bond is known as the bond dissociation energy. More commonly used is the term *bond energy,* which is the energy released when two atoms are brought together to form a bond. The two values are numerically equal but are of opposite sign. For example, the oxygen molecule O_2 has a bond energy of -155 kJ mol^{-1}; the bond dissociation energy is 155 kJ mol^{-1}. This indicates that when two oxygen atoms approach each other and form a molecule (by a σ- and a π-bond) 155 kJ mol^{-1} of energy are *released.*

The nitrogen molecule has one σ-bond and two π-bonds. If the unpaired 2p(x) electrons on the atoms form a σ-bond, π-bonds will be formed in both the y and z planes.

N

Many more complex molecules (e.g. CO_2, C_2H_2) can be explained in terms of σ- and π-bonding, but these will be described later in the course.

It has been assumed that the atoms remain electrically neutral in this bonding. For example, in chlorine molecules each atom has 16 unshared electrons and a half-share in the bonding pair, a net result of 17 electrons. Since this is the same as the number of electrons in a neutral atom, the chlorine atoms in this molecule remain neutral.

But consider the heteronuclear molecule, HF. Heteronuclear means that the molecule is composed of dissimilar atoms. The attractive forces of hydrogen and fluorine for these shared electrons differ because of the different sizes of the atoms, their differing nuclear charges and the efficiency with which the inner electrons shield the nuclear charge. The net result of these differences is that there is a greater probability of finding the bonding electrons in the vicinity of the fluorine atom than of the hydrogen atom. So, instead of the electrons being shared *equally* between these atoms, the fluorine atom has a more than 50 per cent share in them. The fluorine atom now has eight non-bonding electrons ($1s^2\ 2s^2\ 2p_x^2\ 2p_y^2$) and more than a 50 per cent share in the bonding pair ($2p_z^2$). There is a surfeit of negative charge on the fluorine compared to the neutral atom. This, of course, requires a deficiency of electrons on the hydrogen. So the molecule can be written as

$\delta+$ $\delta-$

H — F. The line indicates the covalent bond and the symbol delta (δ) indicates a small quantity. Covalent bonds in which there is this separation of charge are known as *polar covalent bonds*.

Unfortunately it is not possible to predict from basic atomic characteristics the nature of the polarity, since the contributing factors can oppose each other. The main factors are the nuclear charges and atomic sizes of the atoms. As the atomic number increases, the nuclear attraction on the electrons *increases*. However, the atomic size also changes though in a less regular manner. As the principal quantum number increases, the atomic size also increases. This *reduces* the nuclear attraction on the electrons because of the greater distance between the positive nucleus and the negative electrons.

Pauling produced a table of *electronegativity* values which gives the relative forces of attraction on the bonding electrons by the atoms. His results showed that the experimental bond energies were different from the theoretical values. He related the difference to these relative affinities of the atoms for the bond pair. Subsequent workers have improved on the method of estimation, but the values are still of the same order of magnitude as those determined by Pauling. Table 2.1 lists the electronegativity values of a large number of elements. From this table it is found that the values for hydrogen and fluorine are 2.1 and 4.0 respectively. The fluorine has the greater value and so is negatively charged with respect to the hydrogen. This separation of charges in a molecule constitutes a *dipole*: two separated centres of charge. The physical effects of these dipoles are dealt with in the next chapter. The chemical effects become apparent in later chapters.

Table 2.1 Electronegativity values of the elements

H 2.1																	He
Li 1.0	Be 1.5											B 2.0	C 2.5	N 3.0	O 3.5	F 4.0	Ne
Na 0.9	Mg 1.2											Al 1.5	Si 1.8	P 2.1	S 2.5	Cl 3.0	Ar
K 0.8	Ca 1.0	Sc 1.3	Ti 1.5	V 1.6	Cr 1.6	Mn 1.5	Fe 1.8	Co 1.8	Ni 1.8	Cu 1.9	Zn 1.6	Ga 1.6	Ge 1.8	As 2.0	Se 2.4	Br 2.8	Kr
Rb 0.8	Sr 1.0	Y 1.2	Zr 1.4	Nb 1.6	Mo 1.8	Tc 1.9	Ru 2.2	Rh 2.2	Pd 2.2	Ag 1.9	Cd 1.7	In 1.7	Sn 1.8	Sb 1.9	Te 2.1	I 2.5	Xe
Cs 0.7	Ba 0.9	La-Lu 1.1-1.2	Hf 1.3	Ta 1.5	W 1.7	Re 1.9	Os 2.2	Ir 2.2	Pt 2.2	Au 2.4	Hg 1.9	Tl 1.8	Pb 1.8	Bi 1.9	Po 2.0	At 2.2	Rn
Fr 0.7	Ra 0.9	Ac-Lr 1.1-															

Summary

At the conclusion of this chapter, you should be able to:

1. explain how a covalent bond is formed between atoms with unpaired electrons;

2. state the postulates of the Sidgwick—Powell theory which interprets the stereochemistry of a molecule in terms of the number of valence shell electron pairs and the relative repulsive forces of bonding and non-bonding pairs;
3. state that: two electron pairs generate a linear molecule;
three electron pairs generate a trigonal planar distribution;
four electron pairs result in a tetrahedral stereochemistry;
4. describe the mechanism by which boron achieves a covalency of three and carbon a value of four;
5. explain the formation of a dative or coordinate bond;
6. define a Lewis acid and base;
7. distinguish between σ- and π-covalent bonds;
8. describe the formation of multiple bonding in simple molecules;
9. understand the origin of polarity in covalent molecules;
10. use electronegativity values to determine the nature of the charge distribution in a molecule;
11. describe the concept of hybridisation as applied to the formation of sp_3 and sp_2 hybrid orbitals.

Experiments

1. Detection of polarity in a liquid by electrostatic fields (e.g. *Nuffield Advanced Science, Chemistry, Teachers Book I*, Longman, 1970, pp. 204—5).
2. Use modelling balloons to demonstrate the Sidgwick—Powell theory.

References

The Sidgwick—Powell theory of molecular structure; J. J. Cox and C. D. Whiston,
Part I : *Educ. Chem.*, 1970, 7, 93—5;
Part II: *Educ. Chem.*, 1970, 7, 234—40.
The electron-pair repulsion theory for molecular geometry; R. J. Gillespie, *J. Chem. Educ.*, 1970, 47, 18—23.
Inorganic stereochemistry; R. J. Gillespie and R. S. Nyholm, *Quart. Rev.*, 1957, 11, 339—80.
A simple approach to molecular bonding theory; P. G. Perkins, *Sch. Sci. Rev.*, 1967, 48, 408—16.
A new guide to modern valency theory; G. I. Brown (Longman, 2nd edn., 1967).
A complete table of electronegativities; E. J. Little and M. M. Jones, *J. Chem. Educ.*, 1960, 37, 231—3.
Ionic character, polarity and electronegativities; J. K. Wilmhurst, *J. Chem. Educ.*, 1962, 39, 132—4.

Films

Chemical bonding (CHEM Study).

Filmloop

Structure of a covalent molecule (Longman).

Questions

1. Describe the structure of H_2 and Br_2.
2. Describe the structure of PCl_3, H_2S and ClF. What would be the shapes of these molecules?
3. What is meant by the terms 'sigma bond' and 'pi bond'? Illustrate your answer by reference to O_2.
4. Describe the electronic structure of the N_2 molecule.
5. Sulphur forms molecules consisting of rings of S_8 units. Describe the bonding and so the stereochemistry of the molecule.
6. Describe the electronic structure of boron and fluorine. These atoms combine to give boron trifluoride. Describe: (a) the formation of the covalent bonds in this compound; (b) the stereochemistry of the compound; and (c) the expected charge distribution in the molecule.

   Boron trifluoride is a Lewis acid. Explain the meaning of the term and describe why this molecule is a Lewis acid.
7. Ammonia molecules react with hydrogen ions (H^+) to form ammonium ions (NH_4^+). Describe the bonding and shape of this ion.

Chapter 3

The ionic bond

It has been shown that in heteronuclear covalent molecules there is a degree of polarity determined by the electronegativities of the bonded atoms. The charge separation in a carbon—hydrogen bond is small (electronegativity difference = 0.4); in an oxygen—hydrogen bond it is substantially larger (electronegativity difference = 1.4). When the electronegativity difference is more than three units, the charge separation is almost complete as, for example, in lithium fluoride (Fig. 3.1).

Obviously, when the atoms are at the normal bonding distances apart, there is still an attraction by the least electronegative element (lithium in our example). But, as will be apparent later in this chapter, it is possible to separate these atoms by relatively simple means. Consider the electronic environment of these atoms. In a normal covalent bond the single lithium 2s electron would be paired with the unpaired fluorine 2p electron. However, the electron pair can be considered as associated entirely with the fluorine due to the large electronegativity differences (cf. Fig. 3.1 and 3.2). The lithium atom in this compound has a deficiency of one electron compared with the number of protons (3 protons, 2 electrons) and this is denoted by a superscript of one unit positive charge, Li^+. Similarly, fluorine has one electron in excess of the number of protons and it is represented as F^-.

Even before the electronic structures were known, Faraday had noted a difference between compounds such as lithium fluoride and others such as

36

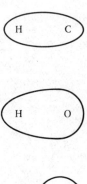

Fig. 3.1 Diagrammatic representation of charge distribution in three bonds

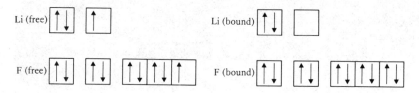

Fig. 3.2 Electronic arrangement in lithium fluoride

tetrachloromethane (carbon tetrachloride). Compounds in the former category conducted electricity when molten or in aqueous solution. The latter compounds did not. Furthermore, in a compound such as lithium fluoride, the fluoride particles approached a positive electrode and the lithium particles approached a negative electrode. He assigned the particles the charge descriptions Li^+ and F^-. To distinguish them from the atoms and other non-conducting particles, he named them *ions*. Consequently we refer to compounds in which there has been a complete transfer of electrons as *ionic compounds*. The ions are held together by powerful electrostatic forces. The bond is described as the electrovalent or ionic bond.

Consider again some of the structures we have described. What is the electronic structure of carbon in tetrachloromethane? On page 27 we saw that it is $1s^2 2s^2 2p^6$ (hybridised). This involves eight electrons in the highest principal quantum number, $n = 2$. What about chlorine in the same compound? It has the structure $1s^2 2s^2 2p^6 3s^2 3p^6$. Again, eight electrons are present in the highest principal quantum number levels, $n = 3$.

In the case of lithium fluoride (Fig. 3.2), fluorine has attained a similar configuration to that of carbon in tetrachloromethane (eight electrons in the $n = 2$ 'shell'). Lithium has only two electrons in the $n = 1$ shell, but, of course, this energy level can only hold two electrons since there is no 1p level.

These electronic structures are the structures of a group of gases of low reactivity, the noble gases:

$1s^2$ helium (cf. lithium in LiF)
$1s^2\,2s^2\,2p^6$ neon (cf. carbon in CCl_4, fluorine in LiF)
$1s^2\,2s^2\,2p^6\,3s^2\,3p^6$ argon (cf. chlorine in CCl_4).

This observation leads to the general rule that elements tend to combine to form compounds in which they have the noble gas structure. The noble gas structure consists of eight electrons, an *octet*. Examine the applicability of the rule to hydrogen (page 22), and to ammonia (page 24).

Even in a case such as boron(III) chloride (page 27) we can see that the rule is not without validity. The boron atom has only a sextet of electrons; but this makes it an acceptor molecule, receiving electron pairs from molecules such as ammonia (page 28).

We find that ionic compounds are normally formed by metals and non-metals which can attain a noble gas structure by the complete transfer of only one or two electrons from, or to, the atoms. For example, in sodium chloride we can depict the formation of an ionic bond as follows:

sodium atom (Na) $1s^2\,2s^2\,2p^6\,3s^1$ chlorine atom (Cl) $1s^2\,2s^2\,2p^6\,3s^2\,3p^5$

$\downarrow$ loss of one electron $\downarrow$ gain of one electron

sodium ion $(Na^+)\,1s^2\,2s^2\,2p^6$ chloride ion $(Cl^-)\,1s^2\,2s^2\,2p^6\,3s^2\,3p^6$
                    (neon structure)   (argon structure)

However, this can be misleading as it does not take into account electronegativity differences which determine the degree of polarity in the bond.

In summary, atoms combine through pairs of electrons, normally attaining a noble gas structure as a result, but the distribution of the electron pair between the two atoms (and so the polarity of the bond molecule) is determined by their electronegativities. In cases in which the electron pair can be considered as concentrated on one atom, rather than between them (electronegativity difference greater than 3), the bond is described as ionic or electrovalent.

Table 3.1 is a rough guide to the relationship between the electronegativity differences of the bonding species and the percentage polarity of the bond.

Table 3.1   Relationship between electronegativities and polarities

Electronegativity difference	0	0.25	0.5	0.75	1.0	1.5	1.75	2.0	2.5	3.0
Percentage polarity	0	2	6	14	22.5	43	52.5	62.5	78.5	89

Table 3.2 gives a comparison of some basic properties of ionic and covalent compounds. The difference in melting points is readily understood by a consideration of the forces between the particles. When a substance

Table 3.2 A comparison of the characteristics of typical ionic and covalent compounds

Bond type:	IONIC	COVALENT
Example	KI	BCl_3
Solubility	Dissolves in polar solvents	Dissolves in covalent solvents
Conductivity	Solutions and liquids conduct electricity	Non-conducting
Melting points	High	Low

melts, the particles constituting the material are more mobile. The ease with which this occurs is determined by the forces holding the particles together. In a covalent chemical there is no substantial intermolecular force (that is forces between molecules; weak forces do exist and are discussed below) and so the molecules are readily separated. In an ionic compound, however, the electrostatic charges on the ions have a three-dimensional effect; they attract not only their associated ions but all their near neighbours (Fig. 3.3).

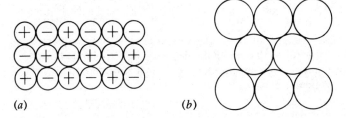

(a)   (b)

Fig. 3.3 Intermolecular forces in (a) ionic and (b) covalent solids
(a) Each ion attracts all neighbouring ions of opposite charge
(b) Neutral molecules exert only weak forces on the neighbouring molecules

The covalent materials have no attraction for electrical charge and so do not carry an electric current. In contrast, the ionic materials do attract electrical charge and so, when free to move (that is when they are molten or in solution) they will conduct electricity.

The process of solution is one of mixing. If two materials are to mix adequately, each particle (molecule or ion) must be in motion and able to interact with every other type of particle present. If a molecule can only interact with its own type of molecule, then they will coalesce, so preventing mixing. When a covalent type of solvent is added to an ionic material, the attractive forces between the ions are too strong to allow the covalent molecules to separate them. If a polar solvent is used, there is interaction between the ions and the solvent making solution possible (Fig. 3.4).

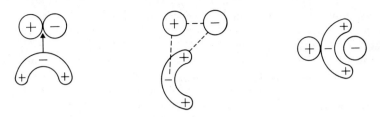

Fig. 3.4 Diagrammatic representation of the mixing of an ionic solute and a polar solvent

Covalent species are able to mix easily with each other because of the lack of strong intermolecular forces.

Ionisation energy

It has been noted that a positive ion (a cation) is formed by the removal of an electron from the atom. This process is known as *ionisation*; the energy required for the process is called the *ionisation energy*. Even for an element in which this is *relatively* easy, the energy involved is high. For example, sodium compounds normally involve sodium ions. The ionisation energy of sodium is 495 kJ mol^{-3}; the molar heat (that is the heat required to raise one mole of the substance through 1 degree Kelvin) for sodium is approximately 27 J. Therefore 495 kJ is equivalent to raising this amount of sodium more than 18000 K! (The unit called the mole is dealt with in Ch. 4.) Obviously it cannot be said that the loss of an electron is easy. Can you suggest where this energy comes from in a chemical reaction? (This will be discussed further in Ch. 13.)

It is possible to measure these energy changes if suitable sources of energy can be found. One possible source is ultraviolet radiation. A simple experimental set-up based on this energy source is illustrated in Fig. 3.5. The vessel containing the sodium is evacuated (to remove air as this would give other chemicals which would also undergo ionisation) and then heated in an

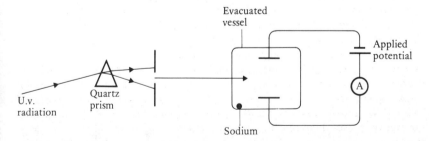

Fig. 3.5 Diagrammatic representation of a photoionisation experiment

oven to vaporise the sodium (so producing sodium atoms). A mercury lamp is used as the source of u.v. light. The radiation is passed through a quartz prism (glass absorbs u.v. radiation) and each wavelength is passed through the heated apparatus in turn. When the radiation is of sufficient energy, ionisation occurs and sodium ions (Na^+) and free electrons are formed. The electric field applied to the system causes migration of the ions and electrons to the appropriate electrodes. This produces a current which is detected by the ammeter. The minimum energy necessary to produce this flow of current is calculated from the wavelength of the incident radiation, since

the energy of radiation = $\dfrac{h \cdot c}{\lambda}$

where h = 'Planck's constant' (6.625×10^{-34} J s)
c = velocity of electromagnetic radiation (2.998×10^8 m s^{-1})
λ = wavelength of the radiation in metres.

An alternative method is to bombard the atoms with high energy electrons. Electrons are generated by a hot filament (Fig. 3.6) and accelerated by an electric field. As before, when ionisation occurs, a current flows through the circuit. The energy necessary is determined by the conversion of the accelerating voltage to energy units.

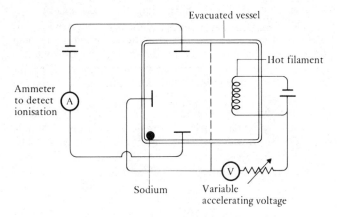

Fig. 3.6 Diagrammatic representation of ionisation by electron bombardment

Of course, with an atomic number of 11 sodium has a number of electrons available for ionisation. How many? An atomic number of 11 indicates the presence of 11 protons; in a neutral sodium atom there will be 11 electrons also. The experiment can be extended to determine successive ionisation energies (Table 3.3). These values can be plotted as a graph (Fig. 3.7; a logarithmic plot is used to minimise the size of the graph). It is observed that the values lie in three groups, namely, the first value, values two

Table 3.3 Successive ionisation energies for sodium   41

Ionisation energies/kJ mol^{-1}

1st	495.85
2nd	4 562.55
3rd	6 912.43
4th	9 543.67
5th	13 353.04
6th	16 610.49
7th	20 114.95
8th	25 490.32
9th	28 934.00
10th	141 364.37
11th	159 076.57

to nine, and the last two values. Compare these results with the description in Chapter 1, Fig. 1.12. The lowest ionisation energy is that of the 3s electron; the second group represents 2p followed by 2s; the last group consists of the 1s electrons. Why are the ionisation energies of the 1s electrons, for example, of different value? Figure 1.12 suggests that they should be of the same value. The first of the 1s electrons to be removed has a repulsive energy due to the other 1s electron helping ionisation. The second electron does not have this repulsive force and so the ionisation energy is slightly higher.

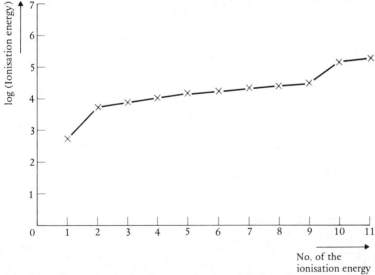

Fig. 3.7   Successive ionisation energies for sodium

Summary

At the conclusion of this chapter, you should be able to:

1. state that ionic bonding is an extreme form of polar bonding;
2. state what is meant by ions;
3. recognise that, as a general rule, elements tend to combine to form compounds in which they have a noble gas structure;
4. describe the formation of ions in compounds such as LiF, NaCl;
5. relate the percentage polarity of a bond to the electronegativity difference of the bonded elements;
6. relate the solubility of a compound to its molecular structure;
7. relate the conductivity of a compound to its molecular structure;
8. relate the melting point of a compound to its molecular structure;
9. define the ionisation energy of an atom;
10. describe at least one method for the determination of the ionisation energy;
11. plot a graph of the successive ionisation energies of a given atom and relate them to the electronic structure.

Experiments

1. Prepare and contrast the properties of anhydrous and hydrated aluminium chlorides.
2. Determine the ionisation energies of the noble gases (see references).

References

Measurement of ionisation potentials of the rare gases; B. E. Dineen and R. S. Nyholm, *J. Roy. Inst. Chem.*, 1963, 110—15.
Ionisation potential of argon by the use of a photocell; A. E. Somerfield, *Sch. Sci. Rev.*, 1966, 48, 162—3.
Experiments on ionisation using a space-charge detector; O. M. White, *Sch. Sci. Rev.*, 1970, 51, 151—3.
Ionic character, polarity and electronegativity; J. K. Wilmshurst, *J. Chem. Educ.*, 1962, 39, 132—4.

Filmloops

Properties of an ionic compound (Longman).
Properties of a covalent compound (Longman).
Evidence for ionisation (Longman).

Questions

1. What do you understand by the terms: (a) ion; (b) polarity; (c) ionisation energy?
2. Describe the bonding in the following compounds, indicating whether you would expect them to be covalent (non-polar), polar covalent or ionic species: (a) HCl; (b) SiF_4; (c) NH_3; (d) MgO; (e) LiCl.
3. The following table gives the successive ionisation energies of an element. Plot the value and discuss the implications of the results.

No. of electron removed	1	2	3	4	5	6	7	8	9	10	11
I.E./kJ mol^{-1} × 10^{-3}:	0.74	1.50	7.70	10.5	13.6	18.0	21.7	25.7	31.6	35.4	169.9

4. Explain in your own words why potassium fluoride: (a) is ionic; (b) forms an electrically conducting solution; (c) has a high melting point; (d) dissolves in water; and (e) has crystals that easily fracture under pressure.

Chapter 4

Crystal structures and molecular properties

Crystal structures

Crystals have fascinated man for many generations. They have been used as objects of beauty by craftsmen and artists alike. If possible, obtain some crystals and examine their characteristics. One of the notable features is the constancy of shape in the crystals of a single substance. This can be explained as resulting from a regular arrangement of the particles (normally atoms or ions) in the solid lattice. Draw a rectangle 86 × 46 mm. How many ½p coins can be fitted into this rectangle? If you use an arrangement as in Fig. 4.1, you should be able to pack 14 into it. You will find that any other arrangement holds fewer coins. So this assembly is known as a close-packing arrangement. A similar system is used for packing circular objects such as apples. The same principle is used in three-dimensions. Arrange a close-packed layer of 'plastic' spheres in a tray. Now introduce another layer of spheres. Where are they more stable? In the gaps between the spheres — for example, in the positions indicated by x in the two-dimensional Fig. 4.1. Notice that when these positions are filled, another close-packed layer is formed.

In metals, the layers consist of atoms in close-packed arrangements. It is relatively easy to deform a metal as there is not a large barrier to movement of one layer over another. In the case of the model using 'plastic' spheres, the hindrance is mechanical; they 'get in the way' of each other. With atoms this

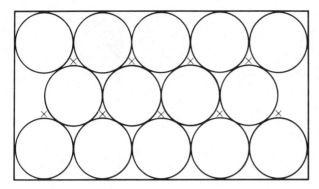

Fig. 4.1 Close-packing arrangement of half-penny coins

steric effect is also operative. Movement can be hindered further by the inclusion of small atoms in the spaces unoccupied by the metal atoms. Typical positions are those gaps left unmarked in Fig. 4.1. For example, iron is less easily worked by the inclusion of carbon to form steel. The carbon atoms hinder relative movement of layers. Similar principles apply in other alloy mixtures. (This is not a complete explanation of alloying properties, but illustrates one effect.)

In ionic compounds we consider the larger ions in the close-packed arrangement. The smaller ions occur in the smaller sites as described for carbon in iron. For example, consider sodium chloride. The ionic radii are Na^+ 95 pm and Cl^- 181 pm. The Cl^- ions are in a close-packed arrangement (see the basic unit, a cube, in Fig. 4.2). In the centre of the diagram, between layers b and c is a space which can be occupied by a sodium ion (Fig. 4.3(a)). This sodium ion acts as a centre of attraction for the neighbouring negative

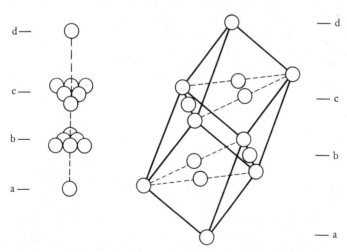

Fig. 4.2 Close-packing of chloride ions in sodium chloride

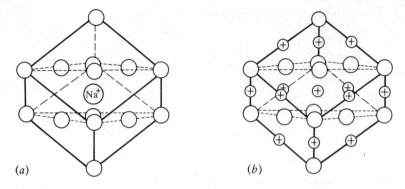

Fig. 4.3 Positions of the sodium ions in a sodium chloride crystal (*a*) and (*b*)

ions, so overcoming their strong repulsion for each other. The ion is a little too large for the site and so there is some displacement of the chloride ions from their nominal positions. The positions of the other sodium ions are as shown in Fig. 4.3(*b*). It will be seen that the sodium ions are in the spaces between the chloride ions.

There are a number of ways in which small ions can be inserted into a close-packing arrangement of larger ions, but the principles described in this particular structure are true of the others as well. It was mentioned above that metals can be easily deformed by the shift of one layer over another — there is little hindrance to such movement. In the ionic lattice we have two new factors — the spaces between layers are filled, so hindering movement (compare this with the comment on alloys), and when a layer is displaced we see that this causes ions of like charge to be closer to each other (resulting in strong repulsion). So, ionic crystals are hard and they also cleave when a shear force is applied to them (Fig. 4.4). A large shear force is required to cause movement because of the steric hindrance, but once displacement is achieved the repulsive forces take effect.

Crystals based on non-polar covalent molecules (for example, iodine) are generally weak, very soft and of low melting points. The iodine crystal

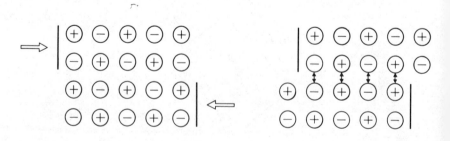

Fig. 4.4 The effect of shear forces in an ionic crystal

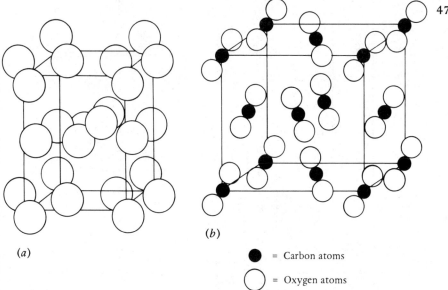

(b)

(a)

● = Carbon atoms

○ = Oxygen atoms

Fig. 4.5 Arrangement in (a) an iodine crystal and (b) solid CO_2

consists of diatomic iodine molecules packed in a manner similar to the close-packing arrangement described above. Movement is easy in each direction since there are only weak forces (see Fig. 4.5) between the molecules.

Polar covalent molecules crystallise with similar arrangements but are harder and less volatile due to the larger intermolecular forces. These arise from attractions between the centres of polarity in adjacent molecules (Fig. 4.6). This is illustrated in ice; the oxygen atoms are in an approximately

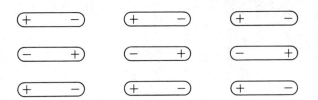

Fig. 4.6 Orientation of polar covalent molecules in a crystal

close-packing arrangement and separated by hydrogen atoms. The water molecules are held in place by strong polar forces between oxygen atoms of one molecule and hydrogen atoms of another (Fig. 4.7).

In some covalent compounds a continuous two- or three-dimensional network of bonds is set up. Graphite consists of layers of linked carbon atoms; diamond involves the same atoms in a three-dimensional array (Fig. 4.8).

Table 4.1 General relationships between structure and properties

	Monatomic	Non-polar molecular	Polar molecular	Giant molecular	Ionic lattice	Metallic
Particle type	Single atoms	Non-polar covalent molecules	Polar covalent molecules	Polymeric units	Ions	Metals
Bonding	Weak	Covalent and weak intermolecular forces	Covalent; electrostatic intermolecular forces	Covalent bonds between units; weak forces between sheets	Electrostatic forces	Metallic bonds with delocalised electrons
Electrical conductance						
(a) solid	Zero	Zero	Very low	Zero	Zero	Very high
(b) liquid	Zero	Zero	Very low	Zero	High	Very high
Solubility in water	Insoluble	Insoluble	Variable. e.g. H_2S, 0.1 M; NH_3, 31 M.	Insoluble	Variable. e.g. NaCl, 6 M; BaO, 0.2 M.	Insoluble

Table 4.1 (*continued*)

	Monatomic	Non-polar molecular	Polar molecular	Giant molecular	Ionic lattice	Metallic
Solubility in covalent solutions	Soluble	Soluble	Soluble	Insoluble	Insoluble	Insoluble
Physical state	Gaseous	Volatile liquids or soft, weak crystals	Soft crystals with little strength and low melting points	Hard crystals with variable strength; high melting points	Hard, brittle crystals with high melting points	Solids; malleable, variable strength; usually high m.p.
Examples	Noble gases	Cl_2, I_2, CH_4, P_4	H_2S, NH_3, CH_3COOH, ICl	Diamond (3-D), graphite (2-D), zeolites (3-D), mica (2-D), asbestos (1-D), red phosphorus (1-D) (D = dimensional)	NaCl, MgF_2, BaO	Metals

50

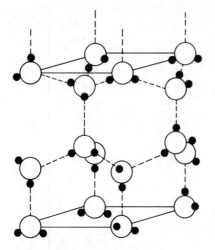

Fig. 4.7   Structure of ice (● = hydrogen atoms; ○ = oxygen atoms)

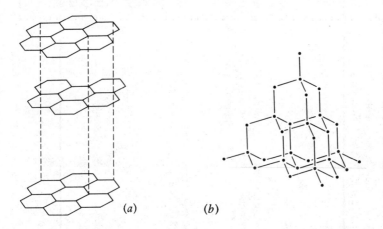

(a)   (b)

Fig. 4.8   Structure of (a) graphite and (b) diamond

Table 4.1 gives a comparison of some typical crystal types and their main properties.

Intermolecular forces

The fact that energy is absorbed in separating even the non-polar covalent molecules from each other is an indication of the presence of some interaction between molecules. Several types of relatively weak intermolecular forces are known.

The forces are electrical in origin and are dependent on the distance between interacting molecules. They are only significant at short distances. Molecules consisting of non-identical atoms are polar (Ch. 2). For example, in the hydrogen chloride molecule, HCl, the molecule is found to have 17 per cent polar character due to chlorine being more electronegative than hydrogen. As a result, there is some orientation because points of opposite charge tend to attract each other (Fig. 4.9). This effect is known as the *Orientation effect*.

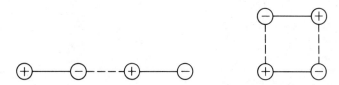

Fig. 4.9   Orientation effects between polar molecules

A closely related effect is the *Induction effect*. In this mode of interaction, the permanent dipole in one molecule induces a dipole in another molecule. The positive charge in one molecule distorts the electron cloud in a neighbouring molecule (a process called polarisation). The distorted cloud sets up another dipole in this molecule (Fig. 4.10) due to the uneven distribution of electronic charge. The larger the molecule, the more easily it is affected by polarisation.

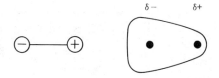

Fig. 4.10   Induced polarity in a molecule by a permanent dipole

We find weak attractive forces in molecules such as nitrogen, hydrogen and the noble gases. These have no permanent dipoles. The forces in these are explained as a *Dispersion effect*. Consider a simple molecule such as hydrogen. In discussing the structure of hydrogen molecules we described the position of the electrons in terms of the most probable position. We found that the most probable position was between the nuclei. But they can be elsewhere for a small portion of the time (Fig. 4.11).

H:H   H·H·   H H: ·H H·   :H H   H⋯H

Fig. 4.11   The variable positions of the electrons in a H_2 molecule. (The first diagram represents the most probable configuration.)

When the pair of electrons is located on one atom only (for example H H:), the bond is polar

$$\overset{+}{H}\ \overset{-}{H}$$

for the short period of time that this configuration lasts. During this time it can induce polarity in another molecule and so mutual attraction. The same effect is possible in a monatomic gas when the electronic charge is greater on one side of a molecule than on the other. Table 4.2 gives some typical values of these forces in different substances.

Table 4.2   Intermolecular forces in some gaseous molecules
(Values are in $J\ cm^6 \times 10^7$)

Gas	Orientation effect	Induction effect	Dispersion effect
He	0	0	1.2
Kr	0	0	110
CH_4	0.003 4	0.057	67.5
HI	0.35	1.68	382
HCl	18.6	5.4	105
NH_3	84	10	93
H_2O	190	10	47

An intermolecular force of larger magnitude, and of wide importance, is one known as the *hydrogen bond*. When hydrogen is bonded to a strongly electronegative atom, the bond is polarised with a positive charge on the hydrogen. If another atom in the vicinity has a negative polarity, there is a strong intermolecular interaction between the two. This force of attraction is usually represented by a broken line (Fig. 4.12).

Fig. 4.12   Examples of hydrogen-bonding

Boiling points of similar compounds normally increase as the relative molecular mass increases. For example, the boiling points of the hydrides of carbon, silicon, germanium and tin increase in a regular manner (Fig. 4.13). In the sequence of the dihydrides of sulphur, selenium and tellurium, this trend is also found. But the first member of the series, water (H_2O), is 'out-of-step'. A similar result is found for the trihydrides of nitrogen (ammonia), phosphorus, arsenic and antimony, and for the hydrides of the halogens. It is observed that the more electronegative elements (oxygen, fluorine, nitrogen and chlorine) are involved in the cases in which abnormally high boiling points are recorded. The reason is that, being the more electronegative, they can form stronger hydrogen bonds. More energy is required for the separation of these molecules to give the vapour phase than would be expected for non-polar molecules.

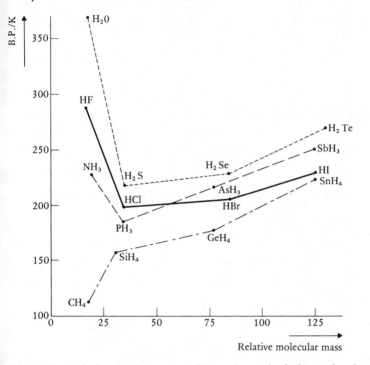

Fig. 4.13 Relationship between boiling point and relative molecular mass

Hydrogen-bonding contributes towards the strength of nylon. Nylon

consists of chains of CH_2 groups joined by the grouping $-\overset{\displaystyle O}{\overset{\displaystyle \|}{C}} - \overset{\displaystyle N}{\underset{\displaystyle O}{|}} -$, which

is known as the amide linkage (Fig. 4.14). The chains are held together through hydrogen bonds between the oxygen and hydrogen atoms of the amide groups. Contrast the strengths of nylon and polyethene, the latter having no hydrogen bonds (Fig. 4.14). Nylon and polyethene have very different tensile strengths, that is the loads they can bear without breaking. This strength is increased if the ease with which one chain shifts over another is reduced. In nylon this is achieved by hydrogen-bonding between the chains. This hinders movement between the chains. Polyethene has no hydrogen-bonding and so the chains have free movement with respect to each other.

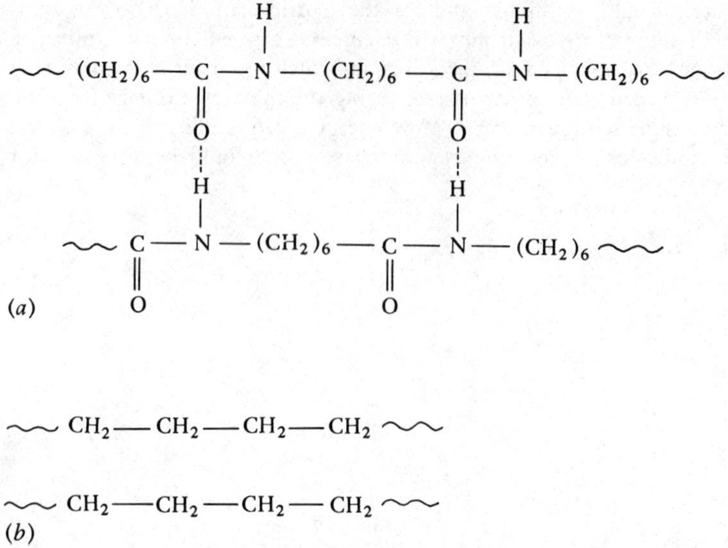

$$\sim\sim (CH_2)_6 - C - N - (CH_2)_6 - C - N - (CH_2)_6 \sim\sim$$

with H atoms on N, O double-bonded to C, and H bonds to N below

(a)

$$\sim\sim CH_2 - CH_2 - CH_2 - CH_2 \sim\sim$$

$$\sim\sim CH_2 - CH_2 - CH_2 - CH_2 \sim\sim$$

(b)

Fig. 4.14 Detail in part of the (a) nylon-6 and (b) polyethene chains

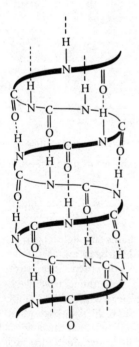

Fig. 4.15 Hydrogen bonds in protein structures

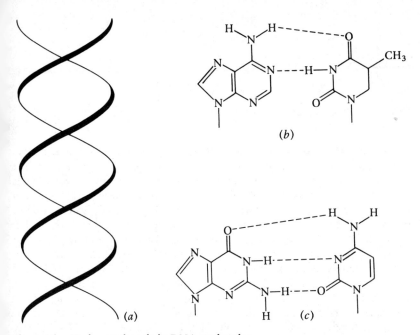

Fig. 4.16 Hydrogen bonds in DNA molecules
((*a*) Double strand of DNA, with hydrogen-bonding between; (*b*) adenine and thymine; and (*c*) guanine and cytosine, which hold the two strands together.)

Closely related to nylon are the naturally-occurring proteins. These also have amide linkages and the hydrogen bonds contribute to the stability of the helical structures of the protein chains (Fig. 4.15). Without hydrogen bonds the proteins would lose most of their important structural and physiological properties. Since proteins occur in a wide variety of biological materials (e.g. muscle, hair, enzymes, etc.), we are obviously very dependent on the hydrogen bonds in living systems. Another molecule of importance to life is DNA. This consists of two strands which are held together through hydrogen bonds (Fig. 4.16). The hard structure of ice, indeed the exceptional properties of water (Ch. 10), can be explained by hydrogen-bonding (Fig. 4.7).

Atomic sizes

In Chapter 1 we described the atomic size for non-bonded atoms in terms of the probability description of the electron. It may be defined alternatively as the *van der Waals' radius*, that is half the internuclear distance between two non-bonded atoms which are in contact. Consider a noble gas in the solid state. The atoms are packed together in a close-packing arrangement. It is possible, from crystallographic data, to measure the internuclear distance. In the case of neon, this value is 320 pm. The radius of each of the atoms making up this distance is 160 pm.

56

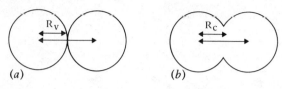

Fig. 4.17 Diagrams showing (*a*) the van der Waals' radius and (*b*) the covalent radius

When the atoms are bonded together, there is a region of overlap so that the areas of maximum probability coincide (page 23). The internuclear distance is now reduced and the radius is known as the *covalent radius* (Fig. 4.17). This is often dramatically different from the van der Waals' radius. For example, the van der Waals' radius of chlorine is 181 pm; its covalent radius is 99 pm. The distance between two atoms depends on the bond order. For example, the carbon to carbon single bond distance is 154 pm (covalent radius, 77 pm) but the carbon to carbon double bond distance is 133 pm (covalent radius, 66.5 pm). (See page 30 for the reason for this difference.) As an approximation it is assumed that the covalent radius of the carbon atom involved in single bonds only is 77 pm. In a compound involving silicon and carbon single bonds we find that the $Si - C$ length is 194 pm. If the carbon radius is 77 pm, then the silicon radius must be $194 - 77 = 117$ pm.

Ionic radii are determined in a similar manner. In a close-packing lattice, the distance between the nuclei of two adjacent identical ions is twice the ionic radius. The distance between ions of opposite charge can be treated in a manner analogous to that for the silicon–carbon bond. For example, the ionic radius for chlorine is 181 pm. The internuclear distance in KCl is 314 pm; therefore, the radius of the potassium ion is $314 - 181 = 133$ pm.

Oxidation numbers

It is useful to have a numerical system that gives some means of describing the extent to which an element has been oxidised or reduced. The early concept of valency is found to be unhelpful because it does not differentiate between bond types and these are not necessarily related to the extent of oxidation. For example, elemental carbon has four covalent bonds in diamond as does carbon in methane. Yet carbon has been reduced in the preparation of methane. Carbon dioxide involves an oxidised state of carbon and this too has four bonds. Carbon monoxide has three covalent bonds; it forms compounds with metals which involve a fourth covalent bond, but the carbon has not been oxidised or reduced.

$C \equiv O \quad (OC)_3Ni \leftarrow C \equiv O$

The oxidation number, or state, concept was introduced to overcome these difficulties. It is defined by R. S. Cahn (in *Introduction to Chemical Nomenclature* 4th edn., Butterworths, 1974, page 12) as: 'The oxidation number of an element in any chemical entity is the charge which would be present on an atom of the element if the electrons in each bond to that atom were assigned to the more electronegative atom.'

In ionic compounds, the bonding electrons have been completely transferred to the more electronegative atom (page 35), so the charge on the ions represents the oxidation state of the element. For example, in potassium iodide ($K^+ I^-$) the potassium has the oxidation number +1 and iodine −1. In calcium oxide ($Ca^{2+} O^{2-}$), the oxidation numbers are +2 and −2 for calcium and oxygen respectively. What are the oxidation numbers of the ions in calcium chloride?

From the electronic structures and the polarity of the atoms, you should be able to show that the formula of calcium chloride is $Ca^{2+} Cl^-_2$. The calcium has the oxidation state +2; the value for chlorine is −1.

The atoms in homonuclear molecules (that is molecules containing only one kind of atom) have oxidation states of zero, since the bonding electrons are equally shared between the atoms.

In order to avoid the necessity of remembering all the electronegativity values, the oxidation states of atoms in covalent molecules can be determined by the following rules. The overall value for the molecule is zero. The atoms are assigned oxidation numbers according to the order of priority given below, so that the overall value is zero:

(a) fluorine has the value −1;
(b) oxygen has the value −2, except in the peroxides when the value is −1;
(c) the other halogens are given values of −1 in the order chlorine, bromine, iodine;
(d) the alkali metals are +1, the alkaline earth metals (e.g. magnesium and calcium) +2;
(e) hydrogen is assigned as +1.

Consider these examples. In methane, the hydrogen has priority over carbon and is given the value +1; so carbon must be −4 to balance the effect of the four hydrogens. Oxygen and fluorine form a compound OF_2; fluorine is −1, therefore oxygen is +2, the fluorine taking precedence over oxygen. Chlorine and oxygen form a similar compound Cl_2O; this time oxygen takes precedence (−2), giving a value of +1 for each chlorine. In hydrogen peroxide, H_2O_2, the oxygen is assigned the value of −1, since it is a peroxide; the hydrogen is, therefore, +1.

For a polyatomic ion such as permanganate, MnO_4^-, the same rules apply except that the whole particle must be considered with its overall charge of −1. The oxygens are −2 each; so $4 \times (-2)$ gives −8 units. The manganese must be +7 so as to leave the net charge of −1:

$$MnO_4^-, +7 + 4(-2) = -1$$

Similarly chromium in dichromate, $Cr_2O_7^{2-}$ must be +6:

$$Cr_2O_7^{2-}, 2(+6) + 7(-2) = -2$$

If, in a reaction, an element goes from a lower to a higher oxidation state it is said to have been oxidised. The reverse process is reduction. Consider the

58 reaction between hydrogen iodide (HI) and oxygen (O_2), giving water (H_2O) and iodine (I_2):

$$2HI + O_2 \rightarrow H_2O + I_2$$

State the oxidation states of hydrogen, oxygen and iodine in both the reactants and the products. Which species have been oxidised and which have been reduced? In HI, iodine is −1, so hydrogen is +1. Oxygen, O_2, being elemental, has a value of zero. In the products, oxygen (in water) is −2, hydrogen +1; the elemental iodine is zero. So, hydrogen is unchanged, iodine is oxidised (−1 to 0), oxygen is reduced (0 to −2).

The mole concept

In chemical reactions, species interact as units: molecules or ions, for example. One molecule of hydrochloric acid reacts with one molecule of sodium hydroxide (strictly, as their constituent ions); two molecules of hydrogen react with one molecule of oxygen. It is, of course, impossible to measure out or examine the reaction of single molecules. It is conventional, therefore, to use a larger quantity. The chosen unit is called the *mole*. It is the quantity of material containing the same number of particles as 12.000 0 g of the carbon-12 isotope. The number of particles in this quantity of carbon (in this case they are atoms) is called Avogadro's number. This figure is not known exactly but it is approximately $6.022\ 17 \times 10^{23}$. We find that 1.007 9 g of hydrogen contain a mole of hydrogen atoms; 2.015 8 g of hydrogen contain a mole of hydrogen molecules; 55.847 g iron contain a mole of iron atoms; 105.989 g of anhydrous sodium carbonate contains a mole of the molecules. It is observed that these values are the relative atomic or molecular masses expressed in grams. Though it has not been proved in this book that this is always the relationship, it may be accepted that this is a statement of general validity. But it should be noted that any quantity of material that contains the specified number of particles can be described as a mole.

In chemical reactions we are concerned with the measurement of volumes more than with weighings, so it is convenient to relate the number of moles to the volume of solution used. The important term is *molarity*. The molarity of a solution is the number of moles in 1 dm^3 of solution. So, a unimolar (1 M) solution contains one mole of solute per dm^3. A 0.1 M solution contains 0.1 mole in 1 dm^3, or 0.025 moles in 0.25 dm^3.

What mass of anhydrous sodium carbonate is required to produce 250 cm^3 of a 0.100 M solution? The relative molar mass is 105.989. So, 105.989 g dissolved in 1 dm^3 would give a 1 M solution. A tenth molar solution would require 10.598 9 g dm^{-3}. In 250 cm^3, $10.598\ 9 \times \dfrac{250}{1\ 000}$ g will be required. 2.649 7 g of the carbonate will need to be measured out.

A solution is prepared from 3.852 g of sodium hydroxide and diluted to 500 cm^3. What is the molarity of the diluted solution? This is equivalent to

$3.852 \times \dfrac{1\,000}{500} = 7.704$ g dm^{-3} The relative molar mass of sodium hydroxide (NaOH) = 39.997. So, the number of moles per dm^3 = $\dfrac{7.704}{39.997}$, that is the solution is 0.193 M.

Partial equations

Chemical equations can be very complex, but it is normally possible to simplify them by limiting the equations to those species (ions or molecules) which actually undergo a change.

When magnesium is added to hydrochloric acid, there are two significant changes: magnesium metal (Mg) dissolves to give magnesium ions (Mg^{2+}), and hydrogen ions (H$^+$) from the acid are discharged as hydrogen gas (H$_2$). The change in the magnesium is represented by a loss of electrons:

$$Mg \rightarrow Mg^{2+} + 2e^-$$

and the hydrogen is released by the gain of electrons:

$$H^+ + e^- \rightarrow \tfrac{1}{2}H_2$$

Since the electron loss in the first situation must balance the electron gain in the second reaction (free electrons do not exist in simple chemical systems), there must be 2 moles of H$^+$ ions discharged per mole of magnesium:

$$Mg \rightarrow Mg^{2+} + 2e^-$$
$$2H^+ + 2e^- \rightarrow H_2$$

These equations may be combined to

$$Mg + 2H^+ \rightarrow Mg^{2+} + H_2$$

The process in which an electron is lost is called *oxidation*; electron gain is *reduction*. Is magnesium oxidised or reduced in this reaction? Since magnesium loses electrons, it must be oxidised. Check this by using oxidation numbers.

Now consider the reaction between hydrochloric acid and sodium carbonate. What changes occur? The hydrogen ions (from the acid) and carbonate ions are converted to water molecules and carbon dioxide. In this case there is no oxidation or reduction and so no electron transfer. This can be established by a consideration of the oxidation numbers of the elements in the reactants and the products.

$$2H^+ + CO_3^{2-} \rightarrow CO_2 + H_2O$$

Why is the chlorine not included in either of the last two examples? Because it is unchanged at the end of the reaction (it is in the form of chloride ions).

Reactions in which there is a change in oxidation state are called redox reactions (*red*uction-*ox*idation reactions). When sulphur dioxide (SO$_2$) is passed into potassium permanganate solution (KMnO$_4$) the purple colour is discharged. The products are manganese ions (Mn^{2+}) and sulphate ions

(SO_4^{2-}). The procedure for balancing redox equations is as follows. (Which of the species in this example are oxidised and reduced? Check using oxidation numbers.)

1. Write down the formulae of the reactants and the products.

   $MnO_4^- \rightarrow Mn^{2+}$
   $SO_2 \rightarrow SO_4^{2-}$

2. Balance the number of atoms of the oxidised or reduced element. In this case, the number of manganese and sulphur atoms are unchanged.

3. Balance the number of oxygen atoms by adding water molecules as necessary.

   $MnO_4^- \rightarrow Mn^{2+} + 4H_2O$ (four oxygen atoms)
   $SO_2 + 2H_2O \rightarrow SO_4^{2-}$ (four oxygen atoms)

4. Balance the hydrogen atoms by the introduction of hydrogen ions as required.

   $MnO_4^- + 8H^+ \rightarrow Mn^{2+} + 4H_2O$ (eight hydrogen atoms)
   $SO_2 + 2H_2O \rightarrow SO_4^{2-} + 4H^+$ (four hydrogen atoms)

5. Balance the charges by adding electrons:

   $MnO_4^- + 8H^+ + 5e^- \rightarrow Mn^{2+} + 4H_2O$ (2+ net charge)
   $SO_2 + 2H_2O \rightarrow SO_4^{2-} + 4H^+ + 2e^-$ (zero net charge)

6. Balance the number of electrons between the equations. The first reaction requires five electrons; the second loses two electrons. Twice the quantities indicated in the first reaction would require ten electrons; five times the quantities in the second equation would release ten electrons:

   $2MnO_4^- + 16H^+ + 10e^- \rightarrow 2Mn^{2+} + 8H_2O$
   $5SO_2 + 10H_2O \rightarrow 5SO_4^{2-} + 20H^+ + 10e^-$

So, 5 moles sulphur dioxide react with 2 moles permanganate.

Work out the half equations for the reaction between iodate(VII) ions (IO_3^-) and iodide ions (I^-), each giving molecular iodine (I_2). The six steps indicated below follow the sequence described above.

1. $IO_3^- \rightarrow I_2$
   $I^- \rightarrow I_2$
2. $2IO_3^- \rightarrow I_2$
   $2I^- \rightarrow I_2$
3. $2IO_3^- \rightarrow I_2 + 6H_2O$
   $2I^- \rightarrow I_2$
4. $2IO_3^- + 12H^+ \rightarrow I_2 + 6H_2O$
   $2I^- \rightarrow I_2$
5. $2IO_3^- + 12H^+ + 10e^- \rightarrow I_2 + 6H_2O$
   $2I^- \rightarrow I_2 + 2e^-$
6. $2IO_3^- + 12H^+ + 10e^- \rightarrow I_2 + 6H_2O$
   $10I^- \rightarrow 5I_2 + 10e^-$

So, 2 moles of iodate (VII) react with 10 moles iodide.

Summary

At the conclusion of this chapter, you should be able to:

1. state that atoms usually pack in a close-packing arrangement in crystals;
2. describe the crystal structure of sodium chloride;
3. describe the crystal structure of a covalent substance;
4. explain the brittle nature of a crystal of an ionic compound;
5. describe the orientation effects in crystals of polar covalent compounds;
6. name and describe some of the intermolecular forces between covalent molecules;
7. describe the hydrogen bond;
8. give details of some examples of hydrogen-bonding;
9. distinguish between van der Waals' covalent and ionic radii;
10. define oxidation number;
11. calculate the oxidation number of an element in a compound;
12. describe an oxidation reaction as one in which the oxidation number of an element is increased;
13. define the mole;
14. define and calculate the molarity of a solution;
15. write partial equations for acid–base and redox reactions;
16. recognise the oxidant and reductant in a chemical equation.

Experiments

1. Experiments to illustrate hydrogen-bonding (see references by J. H. J. Peet and T. A. Whitworth); the heat of mixing of trichloromethane and methyl methanoate (C. M. Ellis, *Educ. Chem.*, 1977, **14**, 18–19).
2. Construction of crystal models (see references).

References

Weak intermolecular interactions; J. E. House, *Chemistry*, 1972, **45**, 13–15.
The origin of intermolecular forces; J. R. L. Swain, *Sch. Sci. Rev.*, 1970, **51**, 808–12.
Some consequences of intermolecular attraction; T. A. Whitworth, *Sch. Sci. Rev.*, 1962, **43**, 401–9.
The nature of van der Waals' forces; J. N. Israelachvilli, *Contemp. Phys.*, 1974, **15**, 159–77.
Hydrogen bond, 'special agent'; V. J. Webb, *Chemistry*, 1968, **41**, 16–20.
The hydrogen bond; J. H. J. Peet, *Educ. Chem.*, 1970, **7**, 199–202.
The hydrogen bond; S. W. Hargreaves, *Sch. Sci. Rev.*, 1961, **43**, 97–104.
The hydrogen bond; J. N. Murrell, *Chem. Brit.*, 1969, **5**, 107–10.
How big is an atom?; J. H. J. Peet, *Phys. Educ.*, 1975, 508–10.

62   *Making Crystal Models;* R. E. Dabby (Pergamon, 1969).
Some aspects of crystal structure; J. W. Coakham, W. Evans and H. Nugent, *Sch. Sci. Rev.*, 1970, 52, 339–50 and 1971, 52, 567–75.
Crystals and Crystal Structure; M. Hudson (Longman, 1971).

Films

Considering crystals (Unilever).
Crystal structure (I.C.I.).
Crystals and their structure (CHEM Study).
Electric interactions in chemistry (CHEM Study).
Oxidation–reduction (McGraw-Hill).
Oxidation numbers and the naming of compounds (*Encyclopaedia Britannica*).

Filmloop

Structure of an ionic crystal (Longman).

Questions

1. Investigate the importance of hydrogen-bonding to every-day life.
2. Describe the differences between the various types of atomic radii.
3. What are the oxidation numbers of the elements underlined in the following formulae?
   (a) $\underline{S}O_2$; (b) $K_2\underline{Cr}_2O_7$; (c) $\underline{H}F$; (d) $Na\underline{H}$; (e) $Mg\underline{F}_2$; (f) $\underline{C}H_4$; (g) $\underline{N}H_3$; (h) $H\underline{N}O_3$.
4. In the following reactions, which elements have been oxidised?
   (a) $Cl_2 + 2HBr \rightarrow 2HCl + Br_2$.
   (b) $MnO_2 + 4HCl \rightarrow MnCl_2 + Cl_2 + 2H_2O$.
   (c) $4HNO_3 + Cu \rightarrow Cu(NO_3)_2 + 2NO_2 + 2H_2O$.
   (d) $2CuCl_2 + 4KI \rightarrow 2CuI + I_2 + 4KCl$.
   (e) $TiCl_4 + 4Na \rightarrow Ti + 4NaCl$.
5. Write partial ionic equations for the following changes and state whether the reactant has undergone oxidation or reduction.
   (a) Nitrate (NO_3^-) → nitrogen dioxide (NO_2).
   (b) Sulphite (SO_3^{2-}) → sulphate (SO_4^{2-}).
   (c) Hydrogen peroxide (H_2O_2) → hydroxide (OH^-).
   (d) Carbonate (CO_3^{2-}) → carbon dioxide (CO_2).
   (e) Hypochlorite (OCl^-) → chloride (Cl^-).
   (f) Permanganate (MnO_4^-) → manganese(II) ion (Mn^{2+}).
   (g) Chromate (CrO_4^{2-}) → dichromate ($Cr_2O_7^{2-}$).
   (h) Iron(III) (Fe^{3+}) → iron(II) (Fe^{2+}).
   (i) Ethanol (CH_3CH_3OH) → ethanal (CH_3CHO).
   (j) Ammonia (NH_3) → nitrate (NO_3^-).

6. Calculate the molarity of solutions containing
   (a) 10.250 g sodium carbonate ($Na_2CO_3.10H_2O$) in 250 cm^3 solution;
   (b) 1.000 g hydrogen chloride (HCl) in 250 cm^3 solution;
   (c) 4.500 g sodium hydroxide (NaOH) in 100 cm^3 solution;
   (d) 12.750 g ammonium chloride (NH_4Cl) in 250 cm^3 solution.
7. What mass of each of the compounds would be required to produce 250 cm^3 of a 0.100 M solution?
   (a) Iron sulphate ($FeSO_4.7H_2O$);
   (b) silver nitrate ($AgNO_3$);
   (c) sodium chloride (NaCl);
   (d) potassium dichromate ($K_2Cr_2O_7$).

Chapter 5

Solutions I: solutions of solids

Diffusion

When two piles of powdered solid are placed next to each other, there is very little tendency to mix. The only mixing occurs at the perimeters of the bases in the positions of contact. This is normally due to gravitational forces causing some particles to run down the sides of the piles, especially if there is any disturbance of the bench (Fig. 5.1).

Fig. 5.1 Limited mixing of two quantities of solid

If liquids are used instead, a noticeable amount of mixing takes place, though it is usually slow. The process can be illustrated by partially filling a test-tube with water and then adding a little coloured solution to the bottom of the tube without disturbing the water (Fig. 5.2). The coloured liquid slowly spreads throughout the water. The process of mixing is even faster with gases. This process is known as *diffusion*.

In these spontaneous changes, the driving force is the movement of the particles themselves. Since the movement is random, they must eventually

Fig. 5.2 Diffusion of two solutions through each other

become evenly distributed throughout the total volume available. Solids do not mix in this way because of the forces holding the molecules or ions together in the particles and because of the other forces between the solid particles (for example, fictional and gravitational forces).

The diffusion can be speeded up by forced mixing, for example, by shaking, stirring or heating the components together. The spontaneous mixing is described as random motion of the molecules or ions. If this is accelerated, then mixing becomes more rapid. For example, the translational kinetic energy of the particles is determined by the temperature. An increase in the temperature increases the kinetic energy of the molecules and so they move faster.

It is also possible to increase the rate of diffusion by introducing attractive forces such as electrodes (to attract charged particles) or chemical reagents with an affinity for the components.

Definitions

When complete diffusion has occurred between two substances to give a homogeneous mixture, the product is known as a *solution*. A homogeneous system is one in which there is no detectable boundary between the components. If sodium chloride is shaken with water, then the ions become dispersed throughout the water so that there is no detectable boundary, that is the particles of sodium chloride cannot be distinguished from those of water. Clay, on the other hand, when dispersed in water gives a mixture in which solid particles are clearly visible. This is a heterogeneous mixture, a *suspension* of clay in water, and not a solution.

A solution can be prepared from mixtures of various phases. Table 5.1 gives some examples of different types of solution.

When discussing solutions we usually refer to one substance being dissolved in another. The component which is present in the smallest quantity (the *solute*) is described as dissolved in the component of larger concentration (the *solvent*). The positions can be reversed if the relative concentrations are changed. For example, on a humid day, the air contains water — the water is the solute and air is the solvent. But air will dissolve in water — the air is the

Table 5.1   Kinds of solution

Type	Example
Solid in a liquid	Salt in water
Liquid in a liquid	Vinegar (ethanoic acid in water)
Gas in a liquid	Oxygen in water
Liquid in a gas	Water in air
Gas in a gas	Air (oxygen in nitrogen)
Liquid in a solid	Amalgams (mercury in a metal, e.g. silver)
Solid in a solid	12 carat gold (a metal, such as copper, in gold)

solute and water is the solvent. The application of the terms solute and solvent is arbitrary, the general practice being as described above. However, it is sometimes convenient to 'break this rule' for the sake of simplicity (see the example with lead ethanoate below).

The *solubility* of a solute in a solvent is described as the quantity of a solute that dissolves in a specified quantity of solvent at a stated temperature. Solubility is temperature dependent. In some cases the solubility changes only slightly with temperature (for example, sodium chloride has a solubility of 36.0 g per 100 g water at 20°C (293 K) and 39.8 g per 100 g water at 100°C (373 K)); other substances have fairly dramatic changes in solubility (for example, lead ethanoate varies from 46 g per 100 g water at 15°C (288 K) to 200 g per 100 g water at 100°C (373 K)). Even though the lead ethanoate is the main component of the solution at the higher temperature (66.67 per cent), generally it would still be called the solute since it is the result of a continuous and limited increase in solubility.

A *saturated solution* is defined as a solution in which undissolved solute is in equilibrium with dissolved solute. For example, if a solution of sodium chloride in water contains 20.0 g per 100 g water at 20°C (293 K) and more solid is added, the additional salt slowly dissolves. When the total amount of dissolved solid is 36.0 g per 100 g water, a state is reached in which no more solid can dissolve without the deposition of some solute. When this system is set up, then equilibrium (page 9) is established and the solution is saturated. It is difficult to show that an equilibrium exists under these conditions, but it can be done by the use of radioactive tracer atoms. For example, if a saturated solution of sodium chloride is prepared in the usual way and to the excess solid radioactive sodium chloride is added, it is found that radioactivity slowly arises in the solution too, even though it was initially saturated with inactive salt. So, some sodium chloride has dissolved, and, since the concentration has not changed, some has also crystallised out of solution.

It should be observed that the concentration of a saturated solution may be described as the mass of the solute per 100 g solvent, as above, or as a molarity (the number of moles of the solute per dm^3 solution). The solubility of sodium chloride is stated to be 36.0 g per 100 g water at 293 K. The density of the solution at this temperature is 1 360 g dm^{-3} (or 1 360 kg m^{-3}).

So, 1 000 g water contains 360 g sodium chloride in a saturated solution. The mass of the solution will be 1 360 g (that is 1 000 g water plus 360 g solute). The volume of the solution is

$$\frac{1\ 360\ g}{1\ 360\ g\ dm^{-3}}$$
$$=1\ dm^3$$

The number of moles of sodium chloride = 360/58.44 = 6.16. Therefore the 6.16 moles sodium chloride are dissolved in 1 dm^3 solution. So the molarity of the solution is 6.16 M.

When a solution is formed there are no detectable physical boundaries between the components of the mixture. The solution is described as a single *phase* system. A saturated solution is a system composed of two phases — a liquid and a solid phase. There is a distinct boundary between the two parts; they can be distinguished visually. A phase is a part of a system which is separated from the other parts by a physically distinct boundary. A liquid in contact with its vapour is a two phase system. Other two phase systems include a solid in contact with its vapour and two immiscible liquids (e.g. oil and water).

Electrolytes

One of the distinctive properties of solutions of ionic compounds in polar solvents, such as water, is their ability to conduct electricity. A compound which, in solution (or in the molten state), conducts electricity is known as an *electrolyte*. Such compounds exist as ions in solution; the positively charged particles are called *cations* (since they travel to the negative electrode or cathode) and the negatively charged particles are called anions (because they migrate to the anode).

When a salt is dissolved in water, the solid (which is already ionic) dissociates into free ions. It is not, therefore, correct to call the process ionisation. A better description is dissociation into ions. However, some substances are covalent in the absence of water and only form free ions on reaction with water. Hydrogen chloride is an example.

$$HCl + aq \rightarrow H^+(aq) + Cl^-$$

The hydrogen ions are solvated (that is combined with solvent molecules; see page 29). In these situations a reaction resulting in ionisation does occur.

Experimental results show that electrolytes can be generally classified into two groups — those that are almost completely dissociated into ions and those that are only partially dissociated at normal concentrations. The degree of dissociation into ions varies with concentration (see below).

Strong electrolytes are those which have high degrees of dissociation into ions. Generally these are substances which are ionic even in the solid state.

Weak electrolytes are those electrolytes which are completely dissociated only in solutions of very high dilution (that is low concentration). Figure 5.3

68

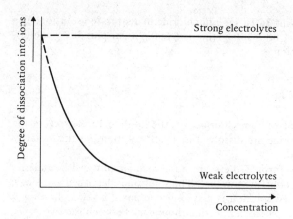

Strong electrolytes

Weak electrolytes

Concentration

Fig. 5.3   How dissociation into ions varies with concentration

illustrates how the fraction of dissociated molecules increases as the concentration decreases. Compounds that fall into this category are mainly polar covalent molecules which form ions on reaction with water.

It should be noted that the terms weak and strong are *not* synonymous with dilute and concentrated.

Table 5.2   Dielectric constants of some liquids

Solvent	Dielectric constant
Hydrogen fluoride (liquid)	84 (273 K)
Water	78.5 (298 K)
Methanol	32.6 (298 K)
Ammonia (liquid)	25.0 (195 K)
Ethanol	24.3 (298 K)
Acetone	20.7 (298 K)
Ether (ethoxyethane)	4.3 (293 K)
Benzene	2.3 (293 K)
Tetrachloromethane	2.2 (293 K)

The ability of a solvent to dissolve an electrolyte is measured by its *dielectric constant*. The dielectric constant of a solvent is a measure of its ability to reduce the attractive force between the ions. It was shown in the previous chapter that ionic substances need polar solvents for solution. The explanation for this was that there is a strong attractive force between ions and this needs to be reduced if solution is to occur.

If the value of the force between two ions in a vacuum is F, then we find that the value in water is $F/78.5$. The value 78.5 is the dielectric constant of water. This value is temperature dependent. Table 5.2 gives some values of dielectric constants for other liquids. From an examination of this data we can determine which solvents are most likely to be suitable solvents for an ionic substance. Benzene, with a low dielectric constant, does not reduce the attractive force between the ions sufficiently to aid solution.

Complexation of ions

An ionic compound can be dissolved by the use of a polar solvent. Alternatively, if it is desired to dissolve the substance in a solvent of low polarity, the charge on the ions must be reduced. This is done conveniently by a process of complexation. A complex compound or ion involves the presence of a coordinate bond (page 28) between an atom or group of atoms (such as H_2O or CN^-) and an ion. The coordinating group is called a *ligand*. One complexing ligand is 8-hydroxyquinoline (Fig. 5.4). This reacts with metal ions (usually in weak acid or neutral solutions) to form covalent compounds. The metal ion becomes part of a covalent complex and is now soluble in an organic solvent such as trichloromethane. Other complexing agents are penta-1, 4-dione, dithizone, dimethylglyoxime, etc.

(a) OH

(b) O—Ag

Fig. 5.4 Structures of (a) 8-hydroxyquinoline and (b) the silver complex

Summary

At the conclusion of this chapter, you should be able to:

1. define diffusion;
2. describe the diffusion processes in solids, liquids and gases and compare the relative rates;
3. define the terms solution, solute, solvent, solubility and saturated solution;
4. give examples of different types of solution;
5. define the terms of electrolyte, cation and anion;
6. state that when a strong electrolyte is dissolved in water it is almost completely dissociated into its ions, whereas a weak electrolyte is only partially dissociated into its ions;
7. state that certain covalent substances react with water to form ions;
8. distinguish between weak and strong electrolytes;
9. distinguish between the strength and the concentration of a solution;

10. define dielectric constant;

11. describe the effect of the dielectric constant of a solvent on its ability to dissolve an ionic compound;

12. state the use of complexing ligands in the extraction of metal ions into covalent solvents.

Experiments

1. Construction of solubility curves (*Selected Experiments in Physical Science*; D. H. Marrow (Longman, 1974, expt. 5.8).
2. Temperature and volume changes on solution (*Nuffield Advanced Science, Chemistry*; (Longman, 1970, expt. 11.2 *b*).
3. Relationship of solubility to the nature of solutes and solvents (ibid; expt. 11.2 *a*).

References

Solubility explained; A. G. Sharpe, *Educ. Chem.*, 1964, 1, 75.

Questions

1. A bottle of ammonia solution was left open on a bench. The ammonia was detected at various positions in the laboratory after differing periods of time. Discuss the movement of the ammonia molecules, assuming there were no draughts.
2. Define the following terms: (*a*) solution; (*b*) solvent; (*c*) solute; (*d*) solubility; (*e*) dielectric constant.
3. Find ten examples of solutions used in every-day life.
4. A stoppered flask containing sodium carbonate solution is cooled so that some ice is formed. What phases are present in the flask?
5. In which of the solvents of Table 5.2 is sodium chloride likely to dissolve?
6. 10.00 g of a calcium bromide solution were carefully evaporated to dryness. The residual solid weighed 0.20 g. What was the concentration of the solution? Calculate the molarity of the solution (density 1.020 g dm^{-3}).
7. 50.0 g of water were saturated with potassium nitrate at 291 K. The excess solid was filtered off and the solution evaporated to dryness. 15.6 g of solid remained. What was the solubility of the potassium nitrate in the water at this temperature?

Chapter 6

Solutions II: solutions of gases and liquids

Solutions of gases in gases

All gases are soluble in all other gases unless a chemical reaction occurs. The mixture obeys the general gas laws and *Dalton's Law of Partial Pressures*. This latter law states that the total pressure of a mixture of gases is equal to the sum of the partial pressures (i.e. the pressures which would be exerted by each of the component gases if it alone occupied the volume of the mixture).

Air consists of 79 per cent nitrogen and 21 per cent oxygen by volume; so the pressures exerted by the two gases are 0.79 and 0.21 of the atmospheric pressure respectively.

Solutions of gases in liquids

The respiration of fish is dependent on the presence of oxygen dissolved in the water. Hard water is formed by the reaction between limestone and carbon dioxide dissolved in water. The solubility of oxygen and carbon dioxide in water is relatively low, but other gases, such as ammonia, are very soluble.

The solubility of gases in liquids is measured in terms of the volume of gas (in dm^3) that can be dissolved in 1 dm^3 of the solvent at a specified temperature and pressure. The volume of the gas is a more convenient term than its mass in this context since the latter is very small. One dm^3 of water is able to dissolve 0.02 dm^3 hydrogen, 1.8 dm^3 carbon dioxide, 80 dm^3 sulphur dioxide or 800 dm^3 ammonia (all at 101.3 kPa pressure). This value (the amount dissolved in 1 dm^3 of solvent at a stated temperature and pressure) is called the *absorption coefficient.*

The solubility is affected by temperature, pressure and the chemical nature of the gas. It decreases with an increase in temperature. The relationship between solubility and pressure is stated in *Henry's law*: The mass of gas dissolved by a given volume of solvent at a given temperature is directly proportional to the pressure of the gas.

Very soluble gases, and those gases that react with the solvent, do not obey Henry's law. In a mixture of gases each gas dissolves as if the others were not present and the amount dissolved depends on the solubility and partial pressure of the particular gas concerned.

The absorption coefficients for oxygen and nitrogen in water at 298 K are 0.04 and 0.02 respectively at atmospheric pressure (101.3 kPa). Atmospheric air is 79 per cent nitrogen and 21 per cent oxygen. What is the composition of dissolved air at this temperature?

For oxygen, 0.04 dm^3 gas dissolve in 1 dm^3 water at 101.3 kPa. The amount of oxygen in the air is 21 per cent by volume; so the pressure exerted by the oxygen is 0.21 of the atmospheric pressure (i.e. 21.2 kPa). Applying Henry's law, if the pressure of oxygen is 0.21 of the atmospheric pressure, then the volume of gas dissolved is 0.21×0.04 dm^3 (in 1 dm^3 water) at 298 K, that is 0.84×10^{-2} dm^3. Similarly, for nitrogen, 0.02 dm^3 gas dissolve in 1 dm^3 water at 101.3 kPa. So, since 79 per cent of the air is nitrogen, it exerts a pressure of 0.79×101.3 kPa (i.e. 80.1 kPa) and the volume of gas dissolved is 0.79×0.02 dm^3 (1.58×10^{-2} dm^3) in 1 dm^3 water at 298 K. The total volume of dissolved gas is 2.42×10^{-2} dm^3. Therefore, the dissolved air consists of 34.7 per cent oxygen and 65.3 per cent nitrogen.

Solutions of gases in solids

When solids dissolve gases there are two distinctive steps — the gases are taken up on the surface of the solid (a*d*sorption) and then diffuse to the inner parts of the solid particles (a*b*sorption).

Heterogeneous catalysis involves the adsorption of reacting gases on the catalyst surface. The formation of solutions of gases on solids can also be used as a means of purifying gases. For example, palladium selectively adsorbs hydrogen.

Gas—liquid chromatography is a means of separating volatile mixtures by differentiating between the solubility of gases in liquids (usually non-volatile oils coated onto solid particles). Gas—solid chromatography is similarly based on the ability of a solid to selectively adsorb gases. In Fig. 6.1 various stages are shown in which one gas from a mixture of two is taken up by a solid more readily than the other one. As the vapour flows along the tube, under

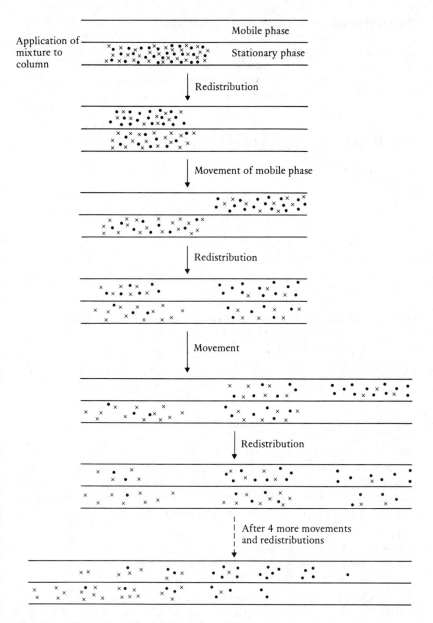

Fig. 6.1 Diagrammatic representation of separation by chromatography

pressure, the components are gradually separated. The component represented by the crosses is adsorbed to a greater extent than is the component shown as dots. After the seven steps shown, the component represented by the dots is more advanced than the component represented by the crosses.

*Equimolar quantities of Non-Volatile Solutes, when
added to Equal weights of the same Solvent lower the V.P
by the same amount. And the ratio of the amt. of lowering
to the V.P of the pure
solvent is equal
to the

ratio of no. of moles
of solute to the no.
of moles of solution. [Raoult's law]

Solutions of liquids in liquids

Liquid solutions are classified according to their miscibility:

(a) completely immiscible liquids – e.g. lubricating oil and water;
(b) completely miscible liquids – e.g. ethanol and water;
(c) partially miscible liquids – e.g. ether and water.

Distillation of miscible liquid mixtures

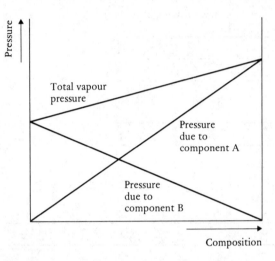

Fig. 6.2   Raoult's law for a miscible liquid mixture

For miscible liquids, the vapour pressure varies with the composition of the mixture. Raoult has formulated a law which equates the total vapour pressure to the sum of the products of the mole fractions (the number of moles of a substance divided by the total number of moles of the components of the mixture) and partial pressures of the components (Fig. 6.2). So,

$$P = x_1 \cdot p_1 + x_2 \cdot p_2$$

where P = total vapour pressure,

p_1 and p_2 are the pressures of components 1 and 2,

x_1 and x_2 are the mole fractions of the respective components.

This is usually restated as: the relative lowering of the vapour pressure of a solvent by a solute is directly proportional to the mole fraction of solute in the solution. Expressed mathematically,

$$\frac{p^{\circ} - p}{p^{\circ}} = \frac{n_1}{n_1 + n_2}$$

where p° and p are the vapour pressures of the solvent and solution respectively and n_1 and n_2 are the number of moles of solute and solvent.

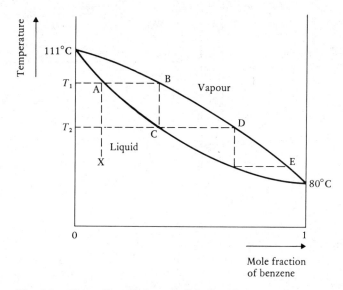

Fig. 6.3 Phase diagram for miscible liquids

Figure 6.3 gives the temperature–composition diagram for a completely miscible system (benzene–methylbenzene). If a liquid corresponding to the point X is boiled, it boils at A to give a vapour of composition B (temperature of boiling, T_1). The liquid is richer in methylbenzene and so boils at a higher temperature. When it reaches its new boiling point, it loses more vapour. The vapour is richer in benzene than the boiling liquid and so the liquid has a higher proportion of methylbenzene than before. The boiling point of the liquid continues to rise until it is $111°C$, that is pure methylbenzene.

Consider the vapour B. If it is condensed to a liquid, this liquid would reboil at a lower temperature (point C) giving a new vapour (D) richer still in the lower boiling component. Repetition of the process will give a vapour E. Eventually the vapour will be pure benzene. This is the principle applied in *fractional distillation*.

Various columns have been designed to facilitate this means of separation (Fig. 6.4). The basic characteristics of these columns are a large surface area and efficient mixing of the vapour and condensed liquids. The packing materials can be beads, pieces of tubing, rings, etc. Figure 6.5 illustrates the procedure. The mixture of composition A boils and the vapour enters the column. B rises up the column until it is condensed by the cooling effect of the surroundings. The condensate, C, runs down the column and is heated by fresh vapour and is reboiled by it. The new vapour, D, rises further up the column since it needs to be cooled down further before it is condensed to a liquid, E. E is reboiled by more rising vapour, so giving vapour F, and so on. The process of condensation and reboiling continues in the column until only the lower boiling component is left to run from the column and the higher boiling component remains in the flask. The rate of heating must be con-

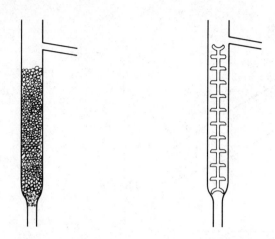

Fig. 6.4 Examples of fractionating columns

trolled so that the lower boiling point (80°C in this case) is not exceeded at the top of the column. If it is exceeded, then vapour originating from a mixture of higher boiling point (e.g. point G) can also leave the column, thereby contaminating the product. Figures 6.6(*a*)–(*c*) illustrate how the boiling points of the issuing vapours change with time of distillation. Initially, only the lower boiling component is evolved. When this is completely removed, no further liquid should be condensed until the higher boiling component is boiled off.

Some liquids do not obey Raoult's law (Fig. 6.7). Liquids with similar chemical properties mix according to Raoult's law. If, however, the molecules of the mixtures have less affinity for each other than do the molecules of the

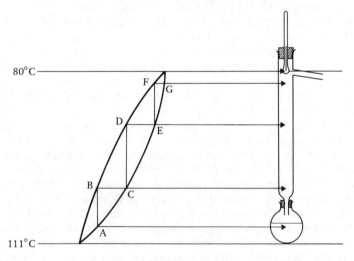

Fig. 6.5 Progress of fractional distillation

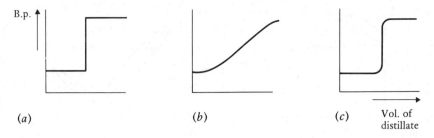

Fig. 6.6 (a) Ideal separation, (b) simple distillation, (c) efficient fractional distillation of a mixture of liquids

pure components, they vaporise more easily than predicted by Raoult's law. So, the vapour pressure is higher and the boiling point of the mixture is lower than expected. A maximum results in the vapour pressure–composition curve (Fig. 6.7(b)), and this is described as a positive deviation from Raoult's law. An example of this is an ethanol–benzene mixture; a maximum occurs for a 95.6 per cent ethanol content. Ethanol and water also have a positive deviation.

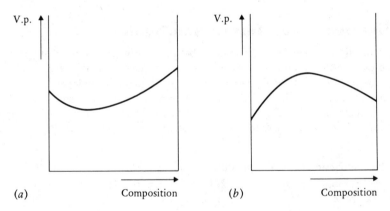

Fig. 6.7 (a) Negative and (b) positive deviations from Raoult's law

When the molecules of the liquid mixture have stronger attractions for each other than that existing in the pure components, then a negative deviation results (Fig. 6.7(a)). Typical examples include nitric acid–water and trichloromethane–methyl methanoate mixtures.

The boiling point curves are given in Fig. 6.8. For nitric acid (Fig. 6.8(a)) the maximum corresponds to 68.2 per cent nitric acid and 121°C. When a solution of any other concentration is distilled, the boiling point gradually rises towards this maximum value. The boiling point and composition of the mixture remain constant at this point and the mixture is called a *constant boiling mixture*, often shortened to C.B.M. These mixtures are also known as *azeotropes*.

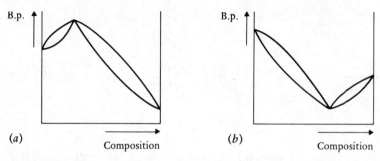

Fig. 6.8 Boiling point diagrams showing (*a*) negative and (*b*) positive deviations from Raoult's law

A similar situation applies with the ethanol–water mixtures (Fig. 6.8(*b*)). In this case the constant boiling mixture has a minimum value (95.6 per cent, 78.2°C). The complete separation of the components by distillation is difficult. One common method is to use a chemical which reacts with one component only. For example, if quicklime is added to the aqueous ethanol azeotrope, the ethanol can be distilled off, the quicklime absorbing the water.

Colligative properties of solutions

Certain physical properties are found to be affected by the number of particles present rather than by their chemical nature. Such properties are called *colligative properties.* In the gaseous phase the gas laws are independent of the chemical nature of the gas; for example, pressure is directly proportional to the number of moles of gas. In solutions there are several such properties and these are of value in determinations of relative molecular masses, for example.

(*a*) Relative lowering of vapour pressure
Raoult's law states that the relationship between the lowering of vapour pressure and the mole fraction can be represented as

$$\frac{p^{\circ} - p}{p^{\circ}} = \frac{n_1}{n_1 + n_2}$$

If a dilute solution is used, n_1 is much smaller than n_2 and so $(n_1 + n_2) \simeq n_2$. In a $0.1\,M$ solution in water, there is 1 mole of solute per 555 moles of solvent, an error which is well within our normal experimental accuracy for these techniques.

Therefore, $\dfrac{p^{\circ} - p}{p^{\circ}} = \dfrac{n_1}{n_2}$

But, the number of moles of substance is determined by the fraction

$$\frac{\text{mass}}{\text{relative molar mass}}$$

$$\frac{p^{\circ}-p}{p^{\circ}} = \frac{w_1 m_2}{w_2 m_1}$$

where w_1, w_2 are the masses of solute and solvent,

$\quad\quad m_1$, m_2 are the relative molar masses of solute and solvent.

If p° and p are measured, and with known values of w_1, w_2 and m_2, it is possible to calculate m_1.

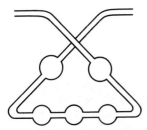

Fig. 6.9 Ostwald–Walker apparatus

A typical experimental procedure is that of Ostwald and Walker. A set of bulbs (Fig. 6.9) is filled with the solution under investigation. This is attached to an identical set containing the pure solvent. Finally a system for collecting solvent vapour is attached. A possible arrangement would involve a set of calcium chloride tubes for trapping water vapour.

The three parts of the apparatus are weighed separately and then a slow stream of air is drawn through the series. The apparatus is reweighed after the airstream is discontinued. The loss of weight from the first set of bulbs is proportional to the vapour pressure of the solution; the net loss from the second set (condensation from the first set and loss due to solvent vapour pressure) is proportional to $(p^{\circ}-p)$. If w_a and w_b are weight losses from the two sets respectively, then

$$\frac{p^{\circ}-p}{p} = \frac{w_b}{w_a}$$

By rearrangement, it can be shown that

$$\frac{p^{\circ}-p}{p^{\circ}} = \frac{w_b}{w_a + w_b}$$

But

$$\frac{p^{\circ}-p}{p^{\circ}} = \frac{w_1 m_2}{w_2 m_1}$$

Therefore,

$$\frac{w_b}{w_a + w_b} = \frac{w_1 m_2}{w_2 m_1}$$

The value $w_a + w_b$ can be obtained directly from the increase in weight of the calcium chloride tubes.

In a typical experiment air was drawn successively through a solution of a sugar (38.89 g per 100 g water) and distilled water, at identical temperatures, and then through anhydrous calcium chloride. It was found that the water lost 0.092 1 g and the calcium chloride tubes gained 5.163 g. By substitution in the above equations,

$$m_1 = \frac{38.89 \times 18.0 \times 5.163}{100 \times 0.092\ 1}$$

$$= 392.4$$

The sugar has a relative molar mass of 392.

(b) Elevation of boiling point

The vapour pressure is dependent on the kinetic energy of the molecules in the liquid phase. Complete evaporation is prevented by the opposing atmospheric pressure. As the temperature is raised, the kinetic energy of the molecules increases and so more molecules escape. When the temperature has been raised sufficiently the vapour pressure becomes equal to the atmospheric pressure. All the liquid then vaporises; the boiling point has been reached. Figure 6.10 gives the variation in vapour pressure with temperature; solution B is more concentrated than solution A. The vapour pressure is depressed on the addition of solute, since the solvent molecules are attracted by solute particles, thereby reducing the solvent volatility. If the vapour pressure is

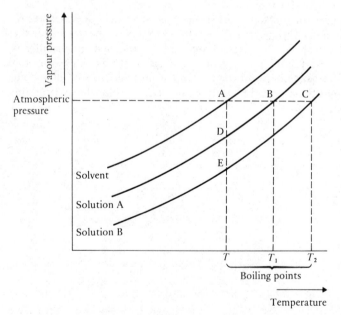

Fig. 6.10   Vapour pressure—temperature relationships

reduced, the boiling point is higher, that is the liquid has to be heated to a higher temperature in order to reach the atmospheric pressure. The sections BD and CE of the curves (Fig. 6.10) are approximately linear if dilute solutions are used. So, the triangles ABD, ACE are similar. Therefore, $\frac{AD}{AE} = \frac{AB}{AC}$ That is the lowering of vapour pressure is proportional to the elevation of the boiling point.

$$\Delta T = T_1 - T \alpha\, p^{\circ} - p$$

But,

$$\frac{p^{\circ} - p}{p^{\circ}} = \frac{w_1 m_2}{w_2 m_1}$$

For a specified solvent, p° and m_2 are constants, so

$$p^{\circ} - p = \frac{k \cdot w_1}{w_2 m_1}$$

Therefore,

$$\Delta T = \frac{k' \cdot w_1}{w_2 m_1}$$

k' is usually replaced by $1\,000 \cdot K_e$, where K_e is the *ebullioscopic* (or boiling point) *constant*:

$$\Delta T = \frac{1\,000 \cdot K_e \cdot w_1}{w_2 \cdot m_1}$$

The constant is the value of ΔT, the boiling elevation, when 1 mole of solute (w_1/m_1) is dissolved in 1 kg solvent. w_2 and w_1 should be measured in identical units, either grams or kilograms. Table 6.1 gives some ebullioscopic constants. Various techniques have been developed for the experimental determination of the boiling point elevations. Particular problems to be overcome are superheating and the small temperature changes.

Table 6.1   Ebullioscopic constants of some common solvents

Solvent	K_e/K kg^{-1}
Water	0.52
Propanone (acetone)	1.72
Ethoxyethane (ether)	2.12
Ethanol	1.15

Cottrell's method (Fig. 6.11) is a typical technique that is successful in the determination of these values. The solvent is gently heated by the action of a small flame on the platinum wire. The liquid boils at the wire. The vapour carries boiling liquid, as a fine spray, through the tube of the funnel and directs it onto the thermometer bulb. The boiling is repeated after the

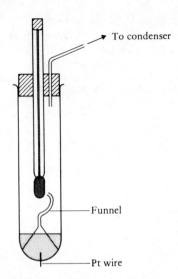

To condenser

Funnel

Pt wire

Fig. 6.11   Cottrell's apparatus

addition of a known mass of solute. The difference in boiling points is recorded on a Beckmann thermometer. The thermometer measures temperature changes over a short range of values to an accuracy of 0.001 K (using a magnifying glass). The $6°$ range of the thermometer is adjustable to the boiling range of the solutions under investigation, the lower point on the scale corresponding to the boiling point of the pure solvent.

Sodium chloride is often added to cooking water. What is the boiling point of a solution containing 0.565 g kg^{-1} of salt?

$$\Delta T = \frac{1\,000 \cdot K_e \cdot w_1}{w_2 \cdot m_1}$$

Substitution in this expression (K_e for water = 0.52 K kg^{-1}) gives

$$\Delta T = \frac{1\,000 \times 0.52 \times 0.565}{1\,000 \times 58.44}$$

$$= 0.005$$

The boiling point of the solution is, therefore, 0.005 K above the normal boiling point of water at this pressure.

(c) Depression of the freezing point

At the freezing point, the solid solvent is in equilibrium with the liquid phase. Since equilibrium exists, the vapour pressures of the solid and liquid phases are equal at this point. Figure 6.12 shows the vapour pressure–temperature diagrams for the liquid and solid phases.

The arguments are similar in this case to those for the boiling elevations. From a consideration of similar triangles (ABD, ACE) we see that the freezing point depression is proportional to the lowering of the vapour pressure.

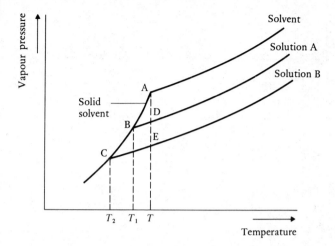

Fig. 6.12   Variation in vapour pressure with temperature

$$\Delta T \propto p^{\circ} - p$$

Also, by similar reasoning, we obtain the expression

$$\Delta T = \frac{1\,000 \cdot K_f \cdot w_1}{w_2 \cdot m_1}$$

where K_f is the *cryoscopic* (or freezing point) *constant* for the solvent. Table 6.2 gives the value of the cryoscopic constant for some solvents.

Table 6.2   Cryoscopic constants for some common solvents

Solvent	K_f/K kg^{-1}
Water	1.86
Benzene	5.12
Ethanoic acid	3.9

The most common method of determining the freezing point depression is that described by Beckmann (Fig. 6.13). A Beckmann thermometer is used and the liquid (pure solvent or solution) is stirred until a constant temperature is reached. At this temperature, freezing occurs. The temperature will usually drop below this value for a short time due to supercooling. The freezing is repeated after a known mass of solute is added and the freezing point depression noted.

Ethan-1,2-diol is added to water as an antifreeze in car radiators. How much ethan-1,2-diol (relative molar mass = 62.07) must be added to 1 dm^3 of

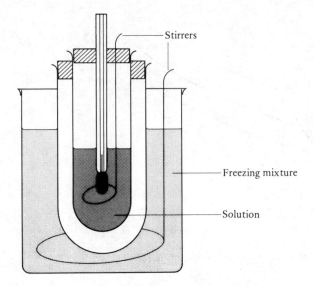

Fig. 6.13 Beckmann's apparatus for cryoscopic determinations

water to prevent the water freezing above $-10°C$ (263 K)? In the formula above

$$w_1 = \frac{10 \times 1\ 000 \times 62.07}{1\ 000 \times 1.86}$$
$$= 333.7$$

The solution must contain 333.7 g ethan-1,2-diol per litre of water.

(d) Osmotic pressure

Nollet, in 1748, found that a membrane made from a pig's bladder was permeable to the solvent in a solution but not to the solute. Such membranes are described as semi-permeable. This can be illustrated by a simple experiment (Fig. 6.14). A thistle funnel is sealed with a taut membrane and attached to a glass tube. The funnel is filled with a concentrated sugar solution and then immersed in a beaker of water. It is found that water enters the funnel, through the bladder, and the liquid level in the tube rises. The level of water continues to rise until the pressure causing the movement of solvent is balanced by the hydrostatic pressure (the pressure due to the liquid column). This process is called osmosis. It is found that osmosis results in the flow of solvent from a less concentrated to a more concentrated solution. Osmotic pressure is the pressure that must be applied to the solution to prevent the flow of solvent through the semi-permeable membrane.

Osmosis is controlled by laws which are similar in form to those which govern the behaviour of gases. These laws are summarised in an equation

$$\pi = C \cdot R \cdot T$$

Fig. 6.14 An example of osmosis

where π is the osmotic pressure and C is the molar concentration. This equation is only fully valid at low concentrations. If the solute is of unknown relative molar mass (m), then $C = w/m$. This method is very useful in the determination of the relative molecular mass of proteins. Solutions which have the same osmotic pressure are called *isotonic*. It will be apparent from the equation that, at constant temperature, solutions of equal molar concentration have the same osmotic pressure.

Osmosis is of great importance in biological systems. The membranes of cell walls are permeable to nutrients and waste products, allowing them to be

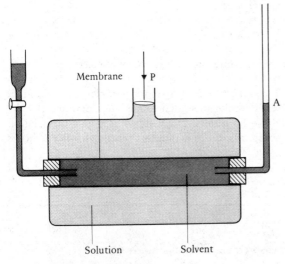

Fig. 6.15 Osmometer

exchanged through the walls. The selectivity of cell walls (and of semi-permeable membranes in general) is complex in mechanism, and involves factors other than size. The medical condition called oedema (an excess of water in the body) can result from a failure of the kidneys to excrete salt properly. An accumulation of salt in the body causes a retention of water. Since osmosis is the flow from a dilute to a concentrated solution, the water does not flow out of the tissues.

Osmotic pressure is measured in an osmometer. A typical construction is that based on the method of Berkley and Hartley (Fig. 6.15). Pressure is applied at P so that there is no change in the liquid level A; it is the pressure that is required to prevent the transfer of liquid across the membrane. A solution of haemoglobin (0.608 g) in water (100 g) gives an osmotic pressure of 202.6 Pa at 273 K. It has been shown that

$$\pi = \frac{w \cdot RT}{m}$$

so

$$m = \frac{(0.608 \times 10^4 \, g \, m^{-3}) \cdot (8.314 \, J \, K^{-1} \, mol^{-1}) \cdot (273 \, K)}{(202.6 \, Pa)}$$

$$= 68 \, 114$$

Haemoglobin is estimated to have a relative molar mass of 68 114. In this calculation it should be noticed that it is necessary to introduce a factor of 10^4 in the concentration since the amount of solvent used is 100 g (= 0.1 dm^3) and the concentration must be quoted as g m^{-3} for consistency in the units.

Limitations

In these experiments based on the colligative properties, there are certain limitations that must be appreciated:
1. the relationships hold only for dilute solutions;
2. the solute is assumed to have no significant vapour pressure, that is it is involatile;
3. only pure solvent crystallises or evaporates in the phase changes;
4. no association or dissociation occurs.

In the latter case, if dissociation occurs, more particles are present in solution. Since these effects are colligative, that is they are determined by the number of particles in solution, a larger effect will be observed if dissociation occurs. Similarly, if the solute associates in solution, then a smaller effect is obtained.

It is possible to derive more complicated relationships than those used which take into account some of these limitations.

Summary

At the conclusion of this chapter, you should be able to:
1. state Dalton's law of partial pressure and Henry's law;

2. define the absorption coefficient;
3. calculate the concentration of a gas in solution from the absorption coefficient and pressure;
4. distinguish between absorption and adsorption;
5. describe the process of separation of the components of a mixture by gas—liquid chromatography;
6. describe the process of fractional distillation;
7. explain the meaning of the term colligative properties;
8. quote Raoult's law;
9. describe experimental procedures for the measurement of the lowering of vapour pressure, the depression of the freezing point, the elevation of the boiling point and the osmotic pressure of a solution;
10. perform calculations to determine the relative molecular mass of a substance given its concentration and the vapour pressure lowering or freezing point depression or boiling point elevation or osmotic pressure.

Experiments

1. Determination of the solubility of carbon dioxide at room temperature and of ammonia at $20°C$ (*Practical Physical Chemistry*; D. Abbott (Dent)).
2. The construction of phase diagrams for two miscible liquids, e.g. cyclohexane—methanol, aniline—hexane, phenol—water. See also the trichloromethane—methyl methanoate system (C. M. Ellis, *Educ. Chem.*, 1977, 14, 18—19).
3. Investigation of the constant boiling mixture for hydrochloric acid and water.
4. Determination of the solubility curve for potassium chloride by silver nitrate estimation of chloride.
5. Examination of the variation in the boiling point and freezing point of water with urea as solute (addition of 0.5 g portions in 25 cm^3 of water). Plot the change in these points against molarity of the solution; hence determine the cryoscopic and ebullioscopic constants. Use these results to determine the relative molecular mass of sucrose.
6. Use of the colligative properties to determine relative molecular masses by such techniques as Cottrell's method and Beckmann's method (*Selected Experiments in Physical Science*; D. H. Marrow (Longman, 1974, exp. 5.11)).

References

Gas Chromatography; R. S. Lowrie (Pergamon, 1969).
Experiments in gas chromatography (Gallenkamp).
Construction of a simple gas—liquid chromatography apparatus (I.C.I.)
Gas chromatography in schools; D. R. Browning (Aimer Products Ltd.).

A demonstration experiment in gas chromatography; G. R. Finch and D. J. S. Sharp, *Educ. Chem.*, 1970, **7**, 242–3.
Chromatography: A Chemical Detective; D. R. Browning (Harrap, 1975).

Films

Gas chromatography (Perkin Elmer).

Filmloops

Mechanism for chromatographic separation (Longman).
Fractional distillation (Longman).

Questions

1. State Henry's law.
   If a sample of air contains 5 per cent carbon dioxide (air pressure 101.3 kPa), what would be the concentration of carbon dioxide in water? (absorption coefficient of CO_2 = 0.878 at 293 K).

2. The table gives the absorption coefficients of some of the components of air at 273 K. What would be the composition of dissolved air? (Assume that atmospheric air contains 1 per cent argon, 5 per cent carbon dioxide, 73.3 per cent nitrogen and 19.7 per cent oxygen.)

Gas	Absorption coefficient at 273 K
Nitrogen	0.023 5
Oxygen	0.048 9
Carbon dioxide	1.713
Argon	0.053 0

3. Describe a method for the determination of the osmotic pressure of a solution.
   A solution containing 10.00 g stachyose in 1 dm^3 aqueous solution has an osmotic pressure of 35.55 kPa at 285 K. Calculate the relative molecular mass of the stachyose.

4. A solution of 0.115 g quinine in 1.36 g camphor has a freezing point of 442.6 K. If the melting point of camphor is 452.8 K and its cryoscopic constant is 39.7 K kg^{-1}, calculate the relative molecular mass of quinine.

5. How would you determine the relative molecular mass of a solute by a boiling point method?
   11.0 g of a solute were dissolved in 100 g trichloromethane and the solution boiled at 337.30 K, compared to the boiling point of the solvent

of 334.20 K. What is the relative molecular mass of the solute?
(K_b = 3.63 K kg^{-1} for trichloromethane.)

6. A solution of glycerol (56.0 g) in aqueous solution (100.0 g) has a vapour pressure at 4.772 kPa at 310 K. If water has a vapour pressure of 6.275 kPa at the same temperature, what is the relative molecular mass of glycerol?

Chapter 7

Colloids and surface tension

In between the well-known and easily recognised extremes of solutions and suspensions, there is another system known as the colloidal dispersion or colloid. The mixture consists of large particles which are dispersed through the medium (often causing it to be slightly opaque) but these particles are not removed by filtration. Normally they are between 10^{-9} and 10^{-7} m in diameter. The particles consist either of large molecules (e.g. high polymers or 'plastics', proteins, DNA) or of aggregates of hundreds or thousands of smaller molecules. These aggregates are known as *micelles*.

A colloidal dispersion is called a *sol* (which means that it is not good practice to abbreviate solution to sol!). If a semi-solid is formed, it is called a *gel*. Rather than use the terms solvent and solute (which apply to true solutions) we use the corresponding terms *dispersion medium* and *disperse phase*. Table 7.1 gives examples of some colloidal systems.

It is often possible to prepare a colloidal dispersion rather than a suspension by a variation of the preparative method. For example, add some dilute hydrochloric acid to a solution of sodium thiosulphate. Sulphur is formed; can it be separated by filtration? Prepare saturated solutions of sulphur dioxide and hydrogen sulphide in water. Dilute the former solution by a factor of ten and add it to hydrogen sulphide solution. Again, sulphur is formed; can it be removed by filtration? Which sample of sulphur is in colloidal dispersion? If this sulphur had to be removed in an analytical

Table 7.1   Classification of colloidal dispersions

Disperse phase	Dispersion medium	Classification	Examples
Liquid	Gas	Fog, aerosol	Mist, clouds
Solid	Gas	Smoke	Dust
Gas	Liquid	Foam	Froth, whipped cream
Liquid	Liquid	Emulsion	Milk
Solid	Liquid	Sol, gel	Paints, jellies
Gas	Solid	Solid foam	Pumice, cork, polyurethane
Liquid	Solid	Solid emulsion	Cheese, butter
Solid	Solid	Solid sol	Alloys, coloured glass

procedure, it would obviously present a problem since it cannot be removed by filtration or centrifugation. It is necessary to find a method for its coagulation (see page 94).

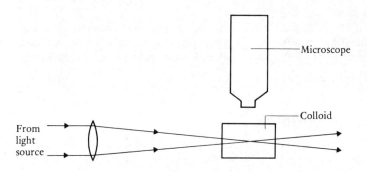

Fig. 7.1   The Tyndall effect

Place the colloidal dispersion in a cell and examine it under a microscope as shown in Fig. 7.1. Focus the light onto the colloid. What do you observe? Now examine a true solution under the same conditions. How do they differ?

The true solution appears to be in darkness (no light is scattered into the microscope). In the colloid, light is scattered showing small specks of light in constant random motion (Fig. 7.2). Each speck of light indicates the position of a colloidal particle. If the progress of one particle is followed and its position is noted at 15-second intervals, a result similar to that in Fig. 7.2 is obtained, in which the dots indicate the positions of the particle at each of these instants. The scattering of the light by the particles is known as the *Tyndall effect,* and the rapid, random motion is known as *Brownian movement.* The Brownian movement is due to the disperse phase particles being bombarded by molecules of the dispersion medium. Because the colloidal particles are relatively small (relative to a suspension), they are easily affected

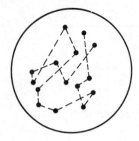

Fig. 7.2 Illustration of Brownian movement

by smaller molecules of the medium. Particles in a suspension are too large to show a noticeable Brownian effect.

Because the colloidal particles scatter light, the colloidal solutions are often partially opaque. The actual light scattered (that is the wavelength of radiation scattered) depends on the particle size. For example, a gold sol with a particle size 6×10^{-8} m appears purple. Particles of half the size appear as a red sol. This provides the basis of a method for the estimation of colloidal particle size.

Colloids differ in their stability. Some colloidal dispersions slowly coagulate on standing; others are apparently stable indefinitely. The unstable colloids are described as *lyophobic* colloids; stable colloids are called *lyophilic* colloids.

Lyophobic colloids

Lyophobes possess little solid–liquid attraction and so the solid particles tend to coagulate. Once coagulated, lyophobic colloids cannot be formed again by the addition of more of the liquid medium. Most metal and salt sols come into this category. They are prepared by chemical reactions under controlled conditions.

A colloidal dispersion of iron(III) hydroxide can be formed by hydrolysis. Add 5 per cent iron(III) chloride solution (10 cm^3) to near-boiling water (250 cm^3).

Arsenic(III) sulphide can be prepared by the reaction between arsenic(III) oxide and hydrogen sulphide. (Care must be taken as both reactants are poisonous. The reaction must be carried out in a fume cupboard.) Boil the oxide (1 g) in water (500 cm^3); cool the solution and pass hydrogen sulphide into it.

Since these colloids are metastable, one would expect coagulation to occur whenever the disperse phase particles collide. The fact that this does not occur indicates the presence of a stabilising force. This is an electrostatic force which arises from the adsorption of ions onto the surface of the particles. (N.B. *ad*sorption rather than *ab*sorption; refer to page 72.) See Fig. 7.3. In this case the adsorbed ions are negatively charged and attract a less strongly held layer of positive ions. Positive sols are formed by the adsorption

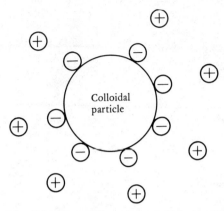

Fig. 7.3   Formation of the Helmholtz double layer

of positive ions. So, when a pair of particles approach each other, they are repelled by their like charges, thereby preventing coagulation. This double layer of charge is known as the *Helmholtz double layer*.

The presence of an adsorbed charge can be illustrated by the fact that these particles are influenced by an electric field. The movement of colloidal particles in an electric field is known as *electrophoresis* (Fig. 7.4). The movement is slow (about 2 cm per hour) and is entirely towards one electrode. For example, an arsenic(III) sulphide sol moves towards the positive electrode. Iron(III) hydroxide is a positive sol and migrates to the negative electrode.

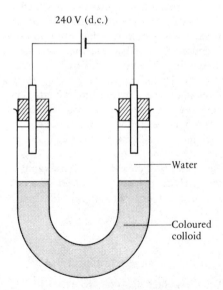

Fig. 7.4   Electrophoresis

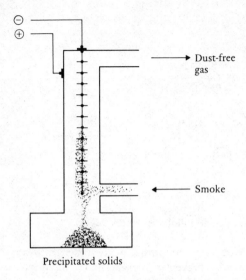

Fig. 7.5 Electrostatic precipitator

The same principle is applied in the electrostatic precipitator used in industry for the removal of dust particles from effluent gases. The smoke is passed through the precipitator (Fig. 7.5) before passing into the atmosphere. A high potential electric field is applied in the precipitator and the electrically charged dust particles are attracted to the electrodes.

A lyophobic colloid can be stabilised by the addition of a small quantity of an electrolyte (providing ions for adsorption). The process in which a precipitate is redispersed into the colloidal state by the addition of an electrolyte is named *peptisation*. An excess of electrolyte has the opposite effect — it causes coagulation of the colloid. This is because the electrolyte neutralises the charge adsorbed on the colloid. The efficiency of an electrolyte in coagulating a colloid is found to be dependent on the charge on the ion which neutralises the adsorbed charge. The relationship is stated in the *Hardy—Schulze law*: the coagulating power of an electrolyte is dependent on its charge. It is found that a divalent ion has one hundred times the coagulating power of a monovalent ion; a trivalent ion is seven times as effective as a divalent ion.

Colloids of opposite charge will cause mutual coagulation. For example, mix the colloidal dispersions of arsenic(III) sulphide (a negatively charged colloid) and iron(III) hydroxide (a positively charged colloid). Both are precipitated.

Lyophilic colloids

These are stable and their formation is reversible. They can be made by the addition of the dispersion medium to the disperse phase; for example, the

dispersion of starch in water. The colloid is stabilised by interaction between   95
the medium and the colloid. The effect of any adsorbed charge on the
stabilisation of the colloid is incidental. The colloid only migrates in an
electric field if there is an adsorbed charge.
Coagulation is difficult. A liquid is added to the mixture such that the
dispersion medium dissolves in it but in which the disperse phase is insoluble.
The effect is to concentrate the mixture by removal of the dispersion
medium.
In contrast to the lyophobes, lyophilic colloids have viscosities substantially greater than those of the pure liquid medium.
Lyophiles can be used to protect lyophobic colloids. The reacting solutions (to prepare the colloid) are mixed in the presence of the lyophile which
acts as the stabiliser. This method is used in the preparation of photographic
films. It can be illustrated by the preparation of silver chloride protected by
gelatine. Solution A is prepared from dilute silver nitrate solution and gelatine
solution. Solution B consists of dilute sodium chloride solution and gelatine
solution. Solutions A and B are mixed. On exposure to light the silver
chloride colloid is converted to a silver colloid.

Dialysis

It is found that many membranes are of selective permeability. They allow
the passage of the solvent and some chemicals. As previously mentioned the
selectivity process is apparently complex and not based on size only (in
contrast to filtration). The process in which there is a net flow of certain
substances through a membrane is known as *dialysis*. This is useful in
purifying colloidal solutions.

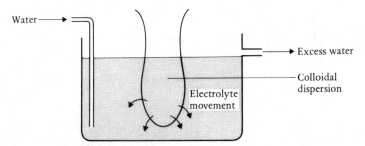

Fig. 7.6   Dialysis using a cellophane membrane

Cellophane is permeable to electrolytes. Therefore, any excess electrolytes are able to pass through such a membrane (Fig. 7.6). The membrane is
not permeable to the colloid and so the colloid and electrolyte can be
separated. Separation is more efficient if flowing water is used. The water can
be tested for the presence of electrolytes. For example, if this is applied to
the iron(III) hydroxide colloid, then the effluent should contain chloride ions

from the hydrolysis reaction. The process can be accelerated by the use of electrodes in the water to attract the ions (electrodialysis).

The process of dialysis operates in the kidneys. Certain toxic chemicals, such as urea, are removed from the blood-stream as the blood passes through the kidneys. Other chemicals that are vital to healthy life, such as sodium chloride, the amino acids and phosphate ions, are not transferred to the urine. Kidney failure, therefore, leads to death by poisoning — the failure of the kidneys to remove these waste chemicals from the blood-stream.

Detergency

When oil is mixed with water, an unstable emulsion is formed; the two liquids separate on standing. A detergent has two effects: it dislodges greases and oils from a fabric and it disperses this dirt throughout the solvent. A detergent has the effect of decreasing the surface tension of a liquid.

When water runs from a pipette, especially in a slow stream, it is found that the liquid exists as a number of small drops (Fig. 7.7(a)). Molecules in the centre of the drop have equal attractive forces (indicated by arrows in the diagram) in all directions. At the surface, however, there is a net inward pull. There is, therefore, a tension in the surface of the drop and this is called the *surface tension*. When the drop is released from the end of the pipette, it forms a spherical drop (Fig. 7.7(b)). If a detergent is added (Fig. 7.7(c); the detergent is represented as ●∿∿) the spherical shape collapses because of reduced surface tension. The detergent molecule consists of an ionic 'head' and a covalent 'tail' (Fig. 7.8). The ionic head is soluble in (i.e. is miscible with) water; the covalent tail tends to be rejected by the water as illustrated (Fig. 7.7(c)).

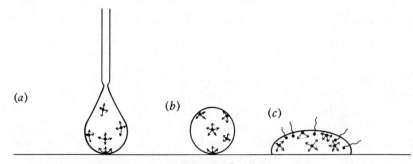

Fig. 7.7 Molecular interactions and surface tension

When a detergent is added to an oily fabric, the covalent end dissolves in the oil and the ionic end in the water. The oil is gradually released from the fabric as the detergent molecules enter the droplet reducing the attraction between the oil and fabric (Fig. 7.9). The oil drops remain suspended because the covalent tails and ionic heads give effective miscibility of the oil and water, and also because the ionic heads cause repulsion of the drops.

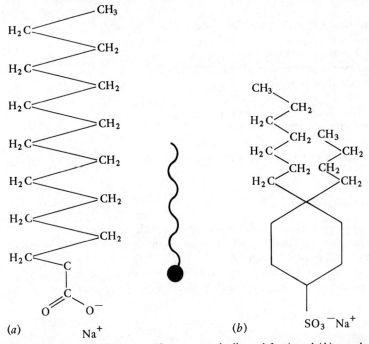

Fig. 7.8 Typical (*a*) soapy (from natural oils and fats) and (*b*) soapless (from mineral oils) detergents

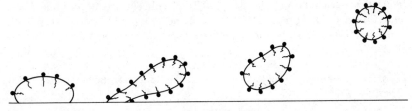

Fig. 7.9 The action of a detergent on a grease stain

A similar surface action occurs in the action of bile (from the gall-bladder) on fats in the body; the large fat droplets could not otherwise be absorbed into the blood-stream. The salts of which the bile is composed have the same structural features as the detergents.

Summary

At the conclusion of this chapter, you should be able to:

1. define the terms sol, gel, micelle, dispersion medium and disperse phase;
2. explain what is meant by a colloid;
3. give examples of the different types of colloid;
4. explain the Tyndall effect and Brownian movement;

5. distinguish between lyophobic and lyophilic colloids;
6. describe the nature of the Helmholtz double layer;
7. describe the process of electrophoresis;
8. describe the action of an electrostatic precipitator;
9. state the meaning of peptisation;
10. quote the Hardy—Schulze law;
11. describe the process of dialysis;
12. state what is meant by a detergent;
13. describe the structure of a detergent;
14. explain the action of a detergent.

Experiments

1. Making an emulsion (Unilever laboratory booklet number 6).
2. Preparation of soapy and soapless detergents (*Nuffield Advanced Science, Chemistry,* Longman, 1970, expt. 18.1).
3. Preparation of colloids — see the experiments described in this chapter.
4. Experiments in detergency (see Shell booklet in references).

References

Principles of the colloidal state; G. D. Parfitt (R.I.C. Teachers Monograph no. 14, 1967).
Experiments in detergency (Shell).
Surface activity; R. J. Taylor (Unilever Education Booklet, Advanced Series, no. 1).
Detergents; E. Moore (Unilever Education Booklet, Ordinary Series, no. 1).
Theory of detergency; R. J. Taylor (Uniliver Education Booklet, Advanced Series, no. 7).

Films

The colloidal state (A.T.V. Ltd.).
Colloids (*Encyclopaedia Britannica*).

Filmloop

Problems in the use of detergents (Nuffield, Longman).

Questions

1. The following list names particles in the colloidal range with their

approximate sizes. Draw scale diagrams of the particles to illustrate their comparative sizes:

rabies (125 nm), influenza virus (100 nm), staphylococcus K (60 nm), gold sol (purple, 60 nm; red, 30 nm), tobacco mosaic (30 nm), poliomyelitis (10 nm), oxyhaemoglobin (5 nm), egg albumin (4 nm).

Compare these with the approximate sizes of small molecules and precipitate particles.

2. Why are car headlights less effective in fog? Why are fog lamps usually yellow?

3. Explain (a) the Tyndall effect, (b) Brownian movement.

4. Distinguish between lyophilic and lyophobic colloids. Give a common example of each.

5. Why is it possible to prepare fairly stable lyophobic colloids?

6. Find out the composition of a fairly typical modern detergent and the function of the various constituents.

Part 2

The Periodic Table

Chapter 8

The periodic classification

There are about ninety naturally-occurring elements and several more elements that have been synthesised in the laboratory. If there were no pattern in, or relationship between, their properties, there would be an extremely large number of facts to study and learn. Fortunately a pattern has been found.

The earliest successful attempt at classification was by Mendeleev. He arranged the elements in order of increasing relative atomic mass, but placed elements with related chemical and physical properties in vertical columns or groups (Table 8.1). The resultant table is known as the Periodic Table.

The rows of elements in his table were known as series; a series is a row of elements up to the repeating unit (the element with the same properties). For example, series 1 is sodium (Na) up to chlorine (Cl), the next element being potassium (K) which has the same properties as sodium. The period represents the cycle from a group I element through to group VIII and includes two series. BUT this definition of a period has been modified because of the modern presentation of the table.

The table has been modified in subsequent years to give an improved interpretation of the chemistry of the elements, but its basic format was still widely used in the 1950s, which is an indication of its acceptability as a basis of discussion of the chemistry of the elements.

It has been found that the chemical properties of the elements are related

Table 8.1   The Periodic Table compiled by Mendeleev (1870)

Groups		I	II	III	IV	V	VI	VII	VIII
Typical elements		H							
		Li	Be	B	C	N	O	F	
Period	**Series**								
1	1	Na	Mg	Al	Si	P	S	Cl	
	2	K	Ca	–	Ti	V	Cr	Mn	Fe Co Ni
2	3	Cu	Zn	–	–	As	Se	Br	
	4	Rb	Sr	Y?	Zr	Nb	Mo	–	Ru Rh Pd
3	5	Ag	Cd	In	Sn	Sb	Te	I	
	6	Cs	Ba	–	Ge	–	–	–	– – –
4	7	–	–	–	–	–	–	–	– – –
	8	–	–	–	–	Ta	W	–	Os Ir Pt
5	9	Au	Hg	Tl	Pb	Bi	–	–	
	10	–	–	–	Th	–	U	–	

to their electronic structures. The Periodic Table has been modified to take into account the electronic structure of the elements as well as their properties. Various forms of table have been described but the most popular is the 'long form' (Table 8.2). The four blocks are known as the s, p, d and f blocks indicating the chemically significant electrons for the elements in those sections. Hydrogen and helium, because of their small sizes and the limitations on the number of electrons in the valence shell, are exceptional in their properties and are generally located and considered separately.

The blocks are also named after the general characteristics of the elements: for example, the s and p blocks, the 'main groups', consist of the active metals and the non-metals respectively (though the latter group does

Table 8.2   Modern Periodic Table

								1 H	2 He								

s block   *p block*   *d block*

3 Li	4 Be											5 B	6 C	7 N	8 O	9 F	10 Ne
11 Na	12 Mg											13 Al	14 Si	15 P	16 S	17 Cl	18 Ar
19 K	20 Ca	21 Sc	22 Ti	23 V	24 Cr	25 Mn	26 Fe	27 Co	28 Ni	29 Cu	30 Zn	31 As	32 Ga	33 Ge	34 Se	35 Br	36 Kr
37 Rb	38 Sr	39 Y	40 Zr	41 Nb	42 Mo	43 Tc	44 Ru	45 Rh	46 Pd	47 Ag	48 Cd	49 In	50 Sn	51 Sb	52 Te	53 I	54 Xe
55 Cs	56 Ba	57 La *	72 Hf	73 Ta	74 W	75 Re	76 Os	77 Ir	78 Pt	79 Au	80 Hg	81 Tl	82 Pb	83 Bi	84 Po	85 At	86 Rn
87 Fr	88 Ra	89 Ac †	104 Rf?	105 Ha?	106												

f block

*	58 Ce	59 Pr	60 Nd	61 Pm	62 Sm	63 Eu	64 Gd	65 Tb	66 Dy	67 Ho	68 Er	69 Tm	70 Yb	71 Lu
†	90 Th	91 Pa	92 U	93 Np	94 Pu	95 Am	96 Cm	97 Bk	98 Cf	99 Es	100 Fm	101 Md	102 No	103 Lr

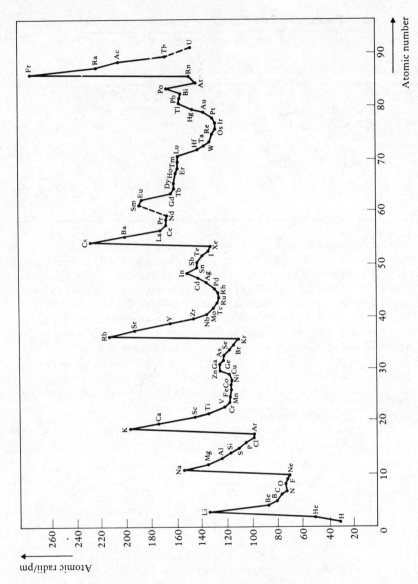

Fig. 8.1 Variation in atomic size with atomic number

also contain some metals). The d block is called the 'transition block' since its properties are intermediate between those of the two main blocks. The f-block elements are described as the 'inner transition elements'.

Apart from the basic chemical properties which characterise an element in a given block and group, there are also significant *trends* in their properties. Perhaps the most important property, because of its fundamental nature, is that of atomic size. Figure 8.1 shows graphically the trend in size. Elements

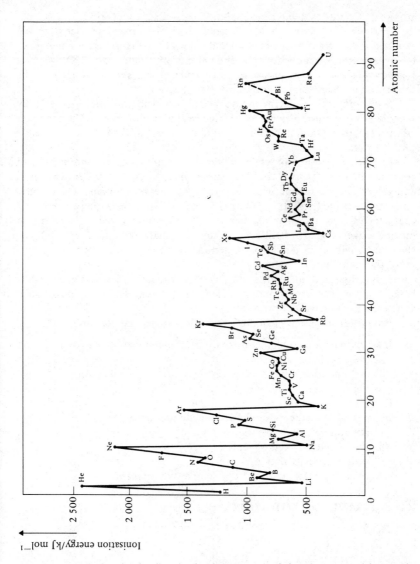

Fig. 8.2 Variation in the first ionisation energy of the elements with atomic number

in the same row, or *period*, involve the same shell of electrons, but, because of the increasing nuclear charge, the atomic size contracts as the atomic number increases; check this by examining the general trend between an alkali metal (e.g. sodium) and a noble gas (e.g. argon). On moving to the next period, the relative size increases because another shell is considered; that is one further from the nucleus; this can be seen by comparing the relative sizes of either the alkali metals or the halogens in Fig. 8.1. So, as a general rule:

atomic size increases down a group, but decreases across a period.

Very closely related to atomic size is the ionisation energy (see page 39). The larger the atom the lower one would expect the first ionisation energy to be, because the attractive force by the nucleus on the electron is acting across a greater distance. A graphical representation of this shows the trend to be the inverse of that observed for atomic size (Fig. 8.2).

Many other characteristics have been plotted in this way — the X-ray spectral energies for the elements (related to the bonding energies of the inner electrons), atomic volumes, and even the distribution of the elements in the earth's crust.

In our description of chemical-bonding, and so of the properties, of compounds we noted that the electronegativities of the constituent elements, and hence the degree of ionic character of the compounds, are a useful quantitative guide (page 35 − 38). It is found that electronegativities and ionic character vary in a regular manner too. The electronegativity decreases on moving down a group (and so any covalent character also decreases); the electronegativity increases across a period, so increasing the covalent character of the compounds.

It is rather more difficult to display chemical properties on a quantitative basis, but this has been done by Allen (see references). Again this regular variation ('periodicity') of properties is observed.

From these results we can draw the following general conclusions:

(a) In a group of similar elements, as the atomic number increases,
   (i) the atomic size increases,
   (ii) the ionisation energy increases
   (iii) the electronegativity decreases,
   (iv) the ionic character of the compounds increases;
(b) In a period of elements, as the atomic number increases,
   (i) the atomic size decreases,
   (ii) the ionisation energy increases,
   (iii) the electronegativity increases,
   (iv) the covalent character of the compounds increases.

Extraction of the metals

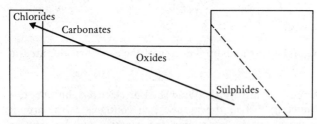

Fig. 8.3 Trends in the occurrence and extraction of the metals (see text for interpretation)

There is also a pattern in the nature of the elements in their mineral sources and in the means required for extraction. Figure 8.3 shows an arrow which

Table 8.3   Extraction processes for the metals

Mineral	Formula	Reduction process
Galena	HgS	Thermal decomposition of the oxide
Zinc blende	ZnS	Carbon reduction of oxide
Haematite	Fe_2O_3	Reduction by C and CO
Pyrolusite	MnO_2	Reduction of oxide with aluminium
Rutile	TiO_2	Reduction of chloride by sodium
Dolomite	$MgCO_3CaCO_3$	Reduction of oxide by silicon
Rock salt	NaCl	Electrolytic reduction

indicates (roughly) the increase in electropositive character. There is a general trend in the mineral nature of the elements which corresponds with this (remember, this is a generalisation). The less electropositive elements tend to occur as sulphides:

PbS	galena
HgS	cinnabar
ZnS	zinc blende
FeS_2	pyrites

As the elements become more electropositive, the oxides are the usual derivatives:

Al_2O_3	bauxite
Fe_2O_3	haematite
Fe_3O_4	magnetite
MnO_2	pyrolusite
TiO_2	rutile

Carbonates are more common with the beryllium group of metals and those of similar chemical nature:

$CaCO_3$	chalk, limestone, marble, etc.
$CaCO_3.MgCO_3$	dolomite
$BaCO_3$	witherite

The alkali metals, the most electropositive elements, occur as the chlorides:

NaCl	rock salt
$KCl.MgCl_2.6H_2O$	carnallite.

The extraction of metals is basically a three-stage process: concentration of the mineral in the ore, extraction of the metal from the mineral, and purification of the metal. The compound used most frequently for extraction purposes is the oxide. This can be obtained by roasting the sulphide in air, or by the thermal decomposition of the carbonate. The extraction process involves a reduction reaction. Why?

The oxide or chloride involves a metal in an ionic or very polar state (for example, Mg^{2+}). To convert this to a metal, the reaction is

$$Mg^{2+} + 2e^- \rightarrow Mg$$

The addition of electrons is reduction. A variety of reducing agents and conditions is available. Table 8.3 gives details of some of the typical processes.

108   The purification procedures are dependent on the properties of the element and those of its impurities. The most common method of purification is an electrolytic method. The impure material is made into an anode; a sheet of pure metal is used as the cathode and the metal salt solution acts as the electrolyte. For example, copper is purified using a pure copper cathode, impure copper anode and a copper(II) sulphate solution as electrolyte.

Summary

At the conclusion of this chapter, you should be able to:

1. explain what is meant by the Periodic Table;
2. describe the structure of the Periodic Table;
3. describe the variation in atomic size, first ionisation energy, electronegativity and covalent character in the Periodic Table;
4. show how the nature of the minerals and the mode of extraction of the metals varies with the position of the element in the Periodic Table;
5. give examples of methods of reduction of minerals to metals.

Experiments

1. Investigate the variation in the appearance and properties of the elements and their compounds in a period of the table.

References

Graphical Representations of the Periodic System During One Hundred Years; E. G. Mazurs (University of Alabama Press 2nd edn., 1974).
Energy Changes in Chemistry; J. A. Allen (Blackie, 1965).
A series of papers on examples of periodicity have been published in Sch. Sci. Rev.: T. M. Earnshaw, 1967, 48, 503–4; D. R. Oldroyd, 1966, 47, 502; J. H. J. Peet, 1968, 49, 814–15; M. P. Wilkinson, 1968, 49, 502–3; E. W. Jenkins, 1967, 49, 193–8.
Principles of the Extraction of Metals; D. J. G. Ives (Royal Institute of Chemistry, 1960).

Film

Chemical families (CHEM Study).

Questions

1. From its position in the Periodic Table, predict as much as you can about

the chemistry of zinc. (Consider its occurrence, extraction, ionisation energy, electronegativity, polarity of its compounds and so their properties, etc.)

2. Investigate the occurrence and extraction of iron and write an account of them.

3. Using the data in Table 2.1, plot the variation in electronegativity values against atomic number. Comment on the result.

Chapter 9

The s-block elements

The s-block elements, even on cursory examination, show distinctive properties. Though metallic, they are clearly different from the d-block elements; they are soft, of relatively low density and very reactive. In this chapter we examine the characteristic properties of these elements. Because of their small size, the 2s elements are not typical and display covalent characteristics. The metals sodium and magnesium (3s), potassium and calcium (4s) are considered to be typical elements.

Metallic bonding

It was seen in earlier chapters that there is a relationship between structure and properties. There are two basic aspects to the structure of these metals: (a) the packing arrangement; (b) the nature of the bonding.

The s-block elements display a type of packing which is distinct from the close-packing arrangement (page 44). This arrangement is the body-centred cubic configuration (Fig. 9.1). This is a lower density configuration than the close-packing system as there are fewer atoms per unit of volume.

There are forces holding the atoms together. The intermolecular forces (Ch. 4) are not sufficiently strong to account for the lower volatility of these elements compared to the non-metals. A new type of bonding is proposed:

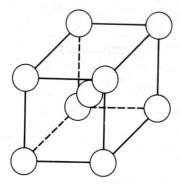

Fig. 9.1 Body-centred cubic arrangement of the alkali metals

the metallic bond. It is most easily interpreted as a lattice of the metal ions in a 'sea' of the 'valence electrons' (i.e. the electrons that are normally used in bonding). For example, the sodium structure would consist of the sodium ions (Na^+, electronic structure 2.8) in the body-centred cubic arrangement with the valence electron ($3s^1$) mobile, continually moving from one atom to its neighbour and so binding these atoms together.

Physical properties

The elements of this group are typified by certain physical properties:
(a) they have low melting points and boiling points compared to the metals of the d and p blocks (Fig. 9.2);
(b) they have relatively low densities;
(c) they, like other metals, are workable (malleable and ductile);
(d) they have a high electrical conductivity in the solid state.

The relatively low melting and boiling points indicate a low binding energy between the atoms (in contrast to the metals of higher atomic number of the same periods). This is confirmed by an examination of the *heats of atomisation* (Fig. 9.3). This is the heat required to separate the atoms from their normal bonding state (in the element) to generate free atoms as in the gaseous state. It can be observed that, generally, the lithium group metals have the lowest binding energies, with the exception of the noble gases which are monatomic gases at ambient temperatures. The binding energy increases as the number of valence electrons increases. In fact, the beryllium group metals have higher binding energies than the first group, because there are twice as many binding electrons.

The s-block elements are also larger than the subsequent elements of their respective periods (Fig. 8.1). The unit volume of these solids will contain, therefore, fewer atoms. This, together with the less dense packing arrangement, results in the relatively low densities of these elements. Table 9.1 lists the densities of some relevant metals. Note the increase in density

112

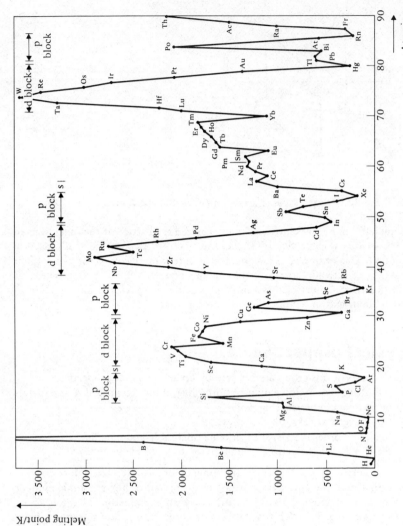

Fig. 9.2 Variation in melting point with atomic number

across a period (decreasing atomic size) and the increase down the group (increasing atomic mass).

The workability of the elements arises from the ease with which one layer of atoms can be moved across another. There is no repulsion due to electrostatic forces and so the brittle nature of the ionic compounds is absent (page 46).

The high electrical conductivity is a natural result of the mobility of the valence electrons. The application of even a low voltage causes the shift of electrons which constitutes a current.

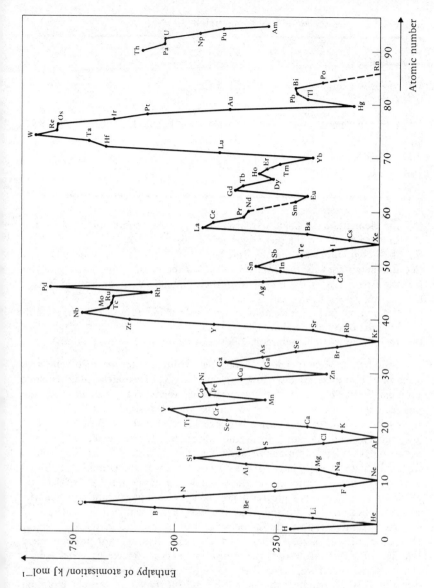

Fig. 9.3 Variation in enthalpy of atomisation with atomic number

Chemical properties

The elements of this block of the Periodic Table are distinctive in their chemical properties as well as in their physical properties:

(a) there is little hydration of the cations;

Table 9.1   Densities/kg m^{-3} of some metals

Li	Be									
533	1 846									
Na	Mg									
966	1 738									
K	Ca	Sc	Ti	V	Cr	Mn	Fe	Co	Ni	Cu
862	1 530	2 292	4 508	6 090	7 194	7 473	7 873	8 800	8 907	8 933
Rb	Sr									
1 533	2 583									
Cs	Ba									
1 900	3 594									

(b) the elements have single oxidation states in their compounds (+1 for the first group, +2 for the second group);

(c) their compounds are mainly ionic;

(d) the metals are very reactive towards other reagents;

(e) the extraction of the metals from their minerals is energetically difficult;

(f) the metals are strong reducing agents;

(g) the compounds are thermally more stable than those of the corresponding salts of other metals;

(h) the ions impart characteristic colours to flames (except magnesium).

Most of these properties can be related directly to the relatively large sizes of the atoms and their low nuclear charges. Because the ions are large (compared with elements in the same period) there is only a small attraction between the nucleus and water molecules of the solvent, since a larger ion means there is a greater distance between the attractive forces of the nucleus and the electrons donated from the water. So, for example, sodium and potassium salts are often anhydrous (as in the chlorides). Those salts which do contain water of crystallisation do not usually have distinctive hydrated ions. In contrast, aluminium (in the p block) forms the ion $[Al(H_2O)_6]^{3+}$ in all of its salts. There is a greater degree of hydration in calcium salts (e.g. the chloride), but this coordinated water is usually easily removed by heating.

As a result of both the decreasing atomic size and increasing nuclear charge on moving across a period, the energy required for the complete removal of an electron (i.e. the ionisation energy) increases. The s-block elements are, therefore, more likely to form ionic compounds than the other elements of the Periodic Table (see Table 3.2 for some effects). The common compounds of this block are ionic. This is reflected in the stability of a large range of their compounds in water (all the simple salts of sodium and potassium are water-soluble) and the properties of the compounds of this block are the properties of the more reactive anions. For example, the carbonates (irrespective of the cation) react with acids to give carbon dioxide; the oxides are hydrolysed to the hydroxides; the hydroxides are bases; the nitrates undergo thermal decomposition; the chlorides, in solution, react with silver nitrate solution to give immediate white precipitates of silver chloride;

$$CO_3^{2-} + 2H^+ \rightarrow CO_2 + H_2O$$
$$O^{2-} + H_2O \rightarrow 2OH^-$$
$$Cl^- + Ag^+ \rightarrow AgCl(s)$$

The cations can have some modifying effect dependent on their electro-negativities. For example, the more electronegative elements of the block (e.g. magnesium) form carbonates which decompose at high temperatures; sodium and potassium carbonates are thermally stable. (The sodium and potassium carbonates will often decompose in glass test-tubes due to the acidic content of the glass.)

$$MgCO_3 \rightarrow MgO + CO_2$$

The nitrates of the s^1 elements (sodium and potassium) decompose to give nitrites; the s^2 elements have nitrates that decompose further to form oxides.

$$NaNO_3 \rightarrow NaNO_2 + \tfrac{1}{2}O_2$$
$$Ca(NO_3)_2 \rightarrow CaO + 2NO_2 + \tfrac{1}{2}O_2$$

The s^1 elements form solid hydrogen carbonates which decompose on heating; the s^2 elements have the corresponding salts in aqueous solution only. Attempts to crystallise or precipitate the latter hydrogen carbonates result in their decomposition. The hydrogen carbonates can be prepared by the reaction of the carbonates with carbon dioxide and water:

$$CaCO_3 + H_2O + CO_2 \rightarrow Ca(HCO_3)_2$$
$$2NaHCO_3 \rightarrow Na_2CO_3 + CO_2 + H_2O$$

These reactions are of significance in two commonplace situations. The dissolution of calcium carbonate from the soil under the action of carbon dioxide and water results in 'hard water'. The carbon dioxide occurs, in part, from the atmospheric gas, but a more significant contribution is made by the carbon dioxide in the soil (from plant and animal respiration) in which the gas has a higher partial pressure. The presence of the salt in water causes a reaction with soaps. These salts (though others are also responsible for hardness of water) are removed by boiling with the consequent precipitation of calcium carbonate. The sodium hydrogen carbonate is the active con-stituent of 'baking powder'. Thermal decomposition generates carbon dioxide (hence the rising of the dough); the presence of weakly acidic salts in the powder can result in the decomposition of the resultant carbonate to increase the efficiency of the powder.

Because of the relative ease of formation of the ions, these elements are the most reactive metals. On exposure to moist air, they form basic oxides and hydroxides very rapidly; these in turn react with acidic gases of the atmosphere to form salts (e.g. the carbonates). An important property, from a safety aspect, is the violent reaction of these elements with water. Sodium reacts rapidly with water giving sodium hydroxide solution and hydrogen. The heat generated in the reaction is sufficient to melt the sodium and boil the water in the vicinity of the metal. As a result, the metal dashes about on the surface as a molten globule on a cushion of steam. If the sodium is prevented from movement (for example, by adhering to the side of the vessel), the heat evolved causes the sodium to ignite. Potassium explodes on contact with water, indicating it has a lower ionisation energy than sodium. (Sodium will explode in the presence of a *small* quantity of water, e.g. with a drop of water or in a moist test-tube.) Calcium and magnesium exhibit reduced chemical activity: calcium reacts rapidly with water but not violently; magnesium reacts slowly with cold water but violently with heated steam. These reactions indicate an important safety factor: care should be taken when using s-block metals; dry instruments and apparatus must be used; the metals should not be placed on a wet bench (for example, when on a filter paper). It is essential to store the metals in an anhydrous environment; they are stored under oil. Calcium and magnesium are normally stored in the dry state, but, unless precautions are taken to prevent it, deterioration occurs due to reaction with the atmosphere. 'Old' samples of calcium are often inert to water because of this; similarly, old samples of magnesium ribbon need to be cleaned of surface products before reaction will occur. They can be stored satisfactorily in a desiccator.

The elements of this block react with a number of non-metals on heating. The reactions on combustion in oxygen are varied: calcium and magnesium form the basic oxides containing O^{2-}; sodium forms the peroxide $(O_2)^{2-}$; potassium forms the superoxide ion, O_2^-. The latter two oxygen ions involve a diatomic species with the charges of -2 and -1 respectively.

$$Ca + \tfrac{1}{2}O_2 \rightarrow CaO$$
$$2Na + O_2 \rightarrow Na^+_2O_2^{2-}$$
$$K + O_2 \rightarrow K^+O_2^-$$

The metals, when heated, react with hydrogen to form hydrides:

$$Na + \tfrac{1}{2}H_2 \rightarrow Na^+H^-$$

Only the s^2 group metals combine directly with nitrogen to form nitrides, e.g. Mg_3N_2. All the s-block metals combine directly with sulphur but the reaction is explosive. They burn in chlorine to form chlorides.

$$Mg + Cl_2 \rightarrow MgCl_2$$

Because of the relative ease with which these elements can lose electrons to form ionic species, the metals are strong reducing agents. For example, sodium is used to reduce titanium(IV) chloride to titanium (see Table 8.3):

$$4Na + TiCl_4 \rightarrow Ti + 4NaCl$$

The reactions of these metals with water, hydrogen, chlorine, oxygen, etc. are all examples of reduction by the metals. The converse of this principle is also true. It is difficult to convert the sodium compounds (for example) such as the chloride and oxide to the metal by chemical reduction. Electrolytic processes are required (see page 107).

Summary

At the conclusion of this chapter, you should be able to:

1. describe metallic bonding;
2. describe a body-centred cublic arrangement;
3. define the heat of atomisation;
4. relate qualitatively the heat of atomisation to the binding energy of the atoms and the number of valence electrons;
5. relate the workability and conductivity of the elements to their structures;
6. state the typical chemical properties of the s-block elements and their compounds, giving examples of each property.

Experiments

1. Compare the ionic volumes of the Na^+ and K^+ ions by adding 4 cm^3 propanone to 0.1 mol of their chlorides in a measuring cylinder.
2. Flame test acidified solutions of the s-block salts.
3. Compare the solubilities of the corresponding salts of sodium (or potassium) and calcium (or magnesium).
4. Determine the hardness of water by titration against 0.04 M sulphuric acid.

References

Extraction of magnesium, in: *Critical Readings in Chemistry;* M. G. Brown (Longman), 1965, 53—6.

Questions

1. For either sodium or potassium, what happens if:
   (a) the metal is added to water;
   (b) the carbonates are added to acid;
   (c) the metals are burnt in oxygen;
   (d) the chlorides are added to silver nitrate solution;
   (e) the nitrates are heated;
   (f) the hydrogen carbonates are heated?
2. For either calcium or magnesium, describe how the metal differs from sodium in its chemical properties.

Chapter 10

The p-block elements

The ionisation energies of the p-block elements are substantially higher than those of the s-block elements; the electronegativities are also higher. So, in general, the properties of the elements of this block are not those associated with metals. Their compounds are mostly covalent. The properties of covalent compounds are described in Table 3.2. Because of the high ionisation energies, ions are not readily formed; metallic bonding (page 110) does not occur. The elements exist as covalent molecules, for example, Cl_2 (page 23), I_2 (page 46), etc.

The properties of the elements and their compounds can be summarised as follows:

(a) the elements, being covalent molecules, are often volatile (either gases, or liquids with low boiling points or solids with low melting and boiling points; e.g. chlorine, bromine and iodine are gas, liquid and solid respectively), non-conducting and of low density;

(b) the oxides are volatile and acidic;

(c) the chlorides are volatile and are hydrolysed by water;

(d) the hydrides are reducing agents;

(e) the elements react with strong oxidising acids;

(f) the elements react with other non-metals (e.g. oxygen, halogens) to form polar covalent compounds and with s-block elements to form ionic species.

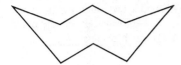

Fig. 10.1 Puckered ring structure of sulphur

There are exceptions to these generalisations (carbon is non-volatile and, in one form, is conducting; silicon dioxide is non-volatile; tetrachloromethane is stable to hydrolysis), but, in general, the properties of even these exceptional elements do fit in with their position in the Periodic Table.

Sulphur is a typical p-block element. The elemental form is S_8, a molecule in which the eight sulphur atoms form a puckered ring (Fig. 10.1). The solid has a melting point of 392 K. Being covalent, it is insoluble in water but it is soluble in carbon disulphide. The density of sulphur is 2.07 g cm^{-3} which is substantially lower than the values for the d-block elements.

Sulphur burns in oxygen to form an oxide, sulphur dioxide (SO_2), which is a gas (b.p. 263 K) which forms an acidic solution in water:

$$SO_2 + 2H_2O \rightarrow H_3O^+ + HSO_3^-$$

With hot concentrated nitric acid, sulphur is oxidised to sulphuric acid (H_2SO_4; sulphurous acid is H_2SO_3):

$$S + 6HNO_3 \rightarrow 2H_3O^+ + SO_4^{2-} + 6NO_2(g)$$

Sulphur reacts directly with hydrogen (for example, when hydrogen is passed through molten sulphur) to form a hydride, hydrogen sulphide (H_2S). This is a reducing agent, and is oxidised to sulphur.

$$H_2S \rightarrow S(s) + 2H^+ + 2e^-$$

Hydrogen sulphide reduces sulphur dioxide to sulphur,

$$SO_2 + 4H^+ + 4e^- \rightarrow S(s) + 2H_2O$$

iron(III) ions are reduced to iron(II) ions,

$$Fe^{3+}(aq) + e^- \rightarrow Fe^{2+}(aq)$$

The hydrides, particularly of the more electronegative first row elements, display hydrogen-bonding (page 52).

When chlorine is passed over heated sulphur, the tetrachloride (SCl_4) is formed. This condenses to a yellow liquid. The liquid undergoes rapid hydrolysis to give an acidic solution, sulphurous acid:

$$SCl_4 + 4H_2O \rightarrow H_3O^+ + HSO_3^- + 4HCl(g)$$

This acid is also formed from sulphur dioxide and water.

Variation in hydrolysis reactions

From Table 2.1 it can be observed that there is a large variation in the electronegativities of the p-block elements. This will affect the polarity of the covalent chlorides of this block. For example, the chlorides of the elements boron, silicon and iodine contain negatively polarised chlorine atoms:

$$\overset{\delta+}{B}\!-\!\overset{\delta-}{Cl}$$

$$\overset{\delta+}{Si}\!-\!\overset{\delta-}{Cl}$$

$$\overset{\delta+}{I}\!-\!\overset{\delta-}{Cl}$$

The polar water molecule reacts with these species so that the negatively charged oxygen attacks the positively charged elements:

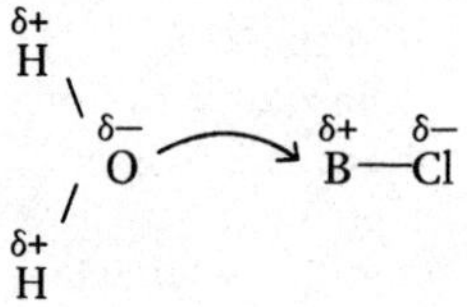

The subsequent reactions involve the replacement of the chlorine atoms by the hydroxo groups, giving an acid:

$BCl_3 + 3H_2O \rightarrow B(OH)_3 + 3HCl$
    (or H_3BO_3) boric acid
$SiCl_4 + 4H_2O \rightarrow Si(OH)_4 + 4HCl$
    (or H_4SiO_4) silicic acid
$ICl + H_2O \rightarrow IOH + HCl$
    (hypoiodous acid)

The hypoiodous acid is unstable and it decomposes to iodine and iodic acid (HIO_3). The chlorides of oxygen and fluorine have a reversed polarity:

$$\overset{\delta+}{Cl}\!-\!\overset{\delta-}{O}$$

$$\overset{\delta+}{Cl}\!-\!\overset{\delta-}{F}$$

The attack will now be of the negative oxygen of water on the positive chlorines:

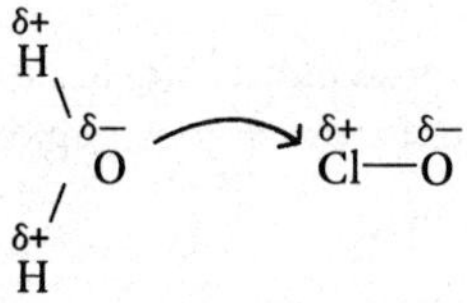

So, instead of the hydrochloric acid formed in the previous examples, hypochlorous acid is formed:

$H_2O + Cl_2O \rightarrow 2HOCl$
$H_2O + ClF \rightarrow HOCl + HF$

Tetrachloromethane, CCl_4, would be predicted to give $C(OH)_4$ since the

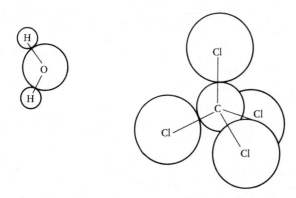

carbon is positively charged. *However,* because of the relatively small size of the carbon atom, it is protected from attack by the water molecules:

Ionic species

It was observed (Ch. 9) that the s-block elements react with non-metals to form ionic compounds; the non-metals have formed anions. While the formation of ionic compounds is dependent on the ease with which metals lose electrons to form cations, obviously the ease of anion formation must also be considered. Figure 10.2 shows the energy change on the addition of an electron to an atom:

$$M + e^- \rightarrow M^-$$

The energy change is known as the *electron affinity.* It can be seen that most elements have negative values, that is energy is evolved on the addition of electrons. For example, chlorine has the value of -348.8 kJ mol^{-1}. In contrast to the ionisation of an atom which involves energy intake, these are energetically favoured processes (since energy is released, which occurs spontaneously in contrast to energy absorption). The positive values occur for elements with fully occupied electron shells (s^2, p^6). The atoms with the lowest values (that is with the most negative values) are the halogens (fluorine, chlorine, bromine and iodine); other p-block elements such as sulphur also have low values (S, -200.5 kJ mol^{-1}). In general, the p-block elements have relatively low electron affinities and so form ionic compounds with elements of relatively low ionisation energies (e.g. the s-block elements). N.B., as with the ionisation energies, the figures are only those of the first electron transfer; a full consideration of the energy changes would have to take into account the number of electrons actually lost or accepted. The formation of anions is a characteristic of the elements of the oxygen and

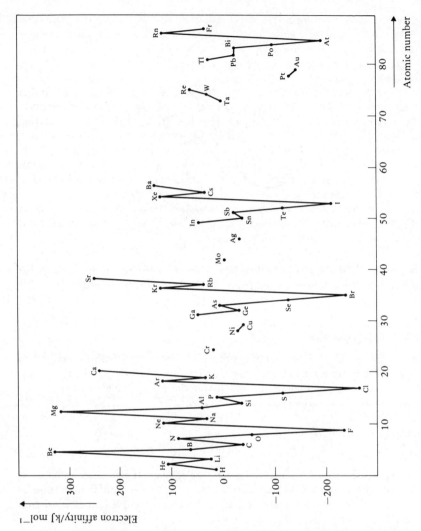

Fig. 10.2 Variation in electron affinity with atomic number

halogen groups of the Periodic Table in particular, though (with suitably strong reducing metals) anions can also be formed with such elements as carbon and nitrogen. For example, sulphur (of the oxygen group) reacts with many metals, on strong heating, to give sulphides.

$$Mg + S \rightarrow Mg^{2+}S^{2-}$$

An examination of Fig. 8.2 shows that the ionisation energies of magnesium and tin are very similar (the increase in nuclear charge in the latter metal is offset partly by its increase in size). Since magnesium forms ions with elements such as chlorine, it is possible that tin, with a similar ionisation energy, might also form cations. It does form an Sn^{2+} ion. By a comparison of the values of the ionisation energies of the s- and p-block elements in Fig. 8.2, can you suggest other p-block elements that might be expected to form cations?

The tendency is most marked in elements to the left of the block and in the lower rows. This is because these elements are larger than the elements in the opposite part of the block. The larger atoms have the lower ionisation energies. An element such as thallium might be expected to form a cation in its compounds (and, in fact, it does); fluorine, on the other hand, is unlikely to do so (one of the highest ionisation energies), though it does form anions. Elements between these extremes of lower ionisation energies and low electron affinities are almost entirely covalent in their properties.

So, all the p-block elements form covalent compounds; the elements at the top of the oxygen and fluorine groups form anions, and the elements at the bottom of the earlier groups form cations.

Another aspect of the ready electron acceptance of these elements is displayed in the formation of complex ions (see page 69). In addition to the formation of simple anions by the transfer of an electron these elements can

$$M + e^- \rightarrow M^-$$

accept the partial transfer of a pair of electrons in a polar molecule or an anion. The feasibility of the process is enhanced if the element is in a positively charged state. For example, aluminium can form Al^{3+} ions (with

$$H_2O + M^+ \rightarrow [H_2O \rightarrow M^+]$$

suitable) reagents such as fluorine. In the presence of water these ions are coordinated:

$$Al^{3+} + 6H_2O \rightarrow [Al(H_2O)_6]^{3+}$$

In fact, most of the cationic species of the p block involve this covalent bonding too. Similarly, phosphorus pentachloride will form a coordinate bond (page 28) with a chloride ion, since the P—Cl bonds are polar:

$$PCl_5 + Cl^- \rightarrow PCl_6^-$$

The same principle applies in the formation of the oxoanions:

$$SO_2 + O^{2-} \rightarrow SO_3^{2-}$$

Variable oxidation states

One other notable characteristic of the p-block elements (in contrast to the s block) is that they display several oxidation states in their compounds. Sulphur, for example, displays several states from -2 to $+6$ (Table 10.1).

As a result of the range of available oxidation states, the compounds of this block can behave as oxidising or reducing agents. Hydrogen sulphide can act as a reducing agent (page 119). Sulphur dioxide can act in either manner. For

Oxidation state   Example

-2	sulphides: ZnS, H_2S
0	sulphur: S_8
$+1$	S_2Cl_2
$+2$	SCl_2
$+4$	SO_2, SCl_4
$+6$	SO_3, H_2SO_4

Table 10.1 Oxidation states of sulphur

example, it oxidises magnesium to magnesium oxide (a change from oxidation number 0 to +2), and it reduces dichromate ions to chromium(III) ions (a change from +6 to +3 in oxidation state).

$$SO_2 + 2Mg \rightarrow 2MgO + S$$
$$3SO_2 + Cr_2O_7^{2-} + 2H^+ \rightarrow 2Cr^{3+} + 3SO_4^{2-} + H_2O$$

Concentrated sulphuric acid can act as an oxidising agent. In the reaction of this acid with copper, the copper is oxidised from the metal to the copper(II) state.

$$H_2SO_4 + 2H^+ + 2e^- \rightarrow SO_2 + 2H_2O$$
$$Cu \rightarrow Cu^{2+} + 2e^-$$

Aluminium

There is, therefore, a range of typical properties of the p-block elements and their compounds. However, there is also some variation within this block as illustrated by a comparison of aluminium and sulphur.

Whereas sulphur forms anions, aluminium forms cations, especially hydrated cations. So, when aluminium is added to an acid it dissolves forming hydrated ions:

$$Al + 3H^+(aq) \rightarrow [Al(H_2O)_6]^{3+}(aq) + 1½H_2$$

The product crystallised from the reaction of aluminium and hydrochloric acid displays typical ionic properties (Table 3.2). Sulphur does not react with acid. Aluminium also reacts directly with chlorine (as does sulphur) to produce a different compound (Al_2Cl_6) which is typically covalent in its properties. This latter compound is volatile, dissolves in covalent solvents, is electrically non-conducting and reacts with water. Sulphur tetrachloride has these same characteristic properties.

Aluminium is metallic in its properties (both physical and chemical). It reacts rapidly with acids to give a salt and hydrogen (see above) but only slowly with water. Sulphur has no reaction with water. The oxide of aluminium, Al_2O_3, is amphoteric, that is it displays both acidic and basic properties. The basic properties are weak (compared to the s-block oxides) but are more significant than the acidic properties. The oxides of sulphur form strong acids.

Aluminium has a single oxidation state, +3, and so its compounds do not display oxidation-reduction properties. Sulphur, with several oxidation states (see above), displays redox properties and has a range of compounds with certain elements, e.g. S_2Cl_2, SCl_2, SCl_4. Aluminium forms only one compound with chlorine or oxygen.

Group properties: The Halogen group

In the s block, group gradations (that is gradual changes in physical and chemical properties) are minimal. In the p block they are more substantial, often varying from non-metals (e.g. carbon) to metals (e.g. lead). The halogen group, though less pronounced in its variation, does show a marked trend even though all the halogens are typical non-metals in their chemical properties.

The properties can be described in terms of their relative oxidising abilities, the common change being from oxidation state 0 to −1.

$$X_2 + 2e^- \rightarrow 2X^-$$

All of the halogens react directly with metals, but they vary in the range of metals that they attack and the extent to which the metals (particularly of the d block) are oxidised. Fluorine reacts with all metals, even with the 'noble metals' (gold, planinum, etc.); the term 'noble' indicates their low degree of reactivity. Chlorine does not attack the less reactive metals very easily.

Bromine and iodine are progressively less reactive. Fluorine usually oxidises a metal to its highest available oxidation state. Because of the decreasing oxidising ability on descending the group, chlorine raises the metal to a lower state than does fluorine; the lower two halogens oxidise it to a lower state still:

$V + 2\tfrac{1}{2}F_2 \rightarrow VF_5$
$V + 2Cl_2 \rightarrow VCl_4$
$V + 1\tfrac{1}{2}Br_2 \rightarrow VBr_3$
$V + 1\tfrac{1}{2}I_2 \rightarrow VI_3$

A similar effect applies with non-metals. Sulphur forms SF_6, SCl_4 and S_2Br_2; iodine does not act on sulphur.

The greater oxidising ability of the higher halogens is reflected in the fact that the halogens can displace from solution, by oxidation, any halides below them in the table. For example, if chlorine is passed into an iodide solution, iodine is liberated. But, iodine cannot displace the higher halogens from their salts.

$Cl_2 + 2I^- \longrightarrow I_2 + 2Cl^-$
$I_2 + 2Br^- \nrightarrow Br_2 + 2I^-$

This is because the higher halogens have a greater affinity for electrons (i.e. are more likely to form anions) than does iodine. This type of reaction is used as a means of extracting bromine from sea-water in which it exists as bromide ions. After removal of insoluble matter, the sea-water is acidified (to pH 3.5) and then treated with chlorine to liberate bromine; the bromine is displaced from the solution by a current of air (an illustration of the volatility of

$$Cl_2 + 2Br^- \rightarrow Br_2 + 2Cl^-$$

bromine). Though weak in its oxidising properties, iodine does have some oxidising ability; it oxidises metals to their iodides (see above) and thiosulphate ions ($S_2O_3^{2-}$) to tetrathionate ions ($S_4O_6^{2-}$), a useful analytical reaction.

The differing oxidising abilities of the halogens are illustrated in their action on water. Fluorine oxidises water to oxygen (though the formation of an intermediate hypofluorous acid, HOF, has also been reported). Chlorine and bromine produce the hypohalous acids, HOCl and HOBr:

$$X_2 + 2H_2O \rightarrow H_3O^+ + X^- + HOX$$

but iodine is unable to attack water.

Since fluorine and chlorine are readily converted to the halides, it would be anticipated that the reverse process is more difficult. In fact, the extraction of fluorine from fluoride is difficult and the oxidation is performed electrolytically. Strong oxidising agents are required for the extraction of chlorine, electrochemical techniques being used as the primary industrial method. An old method which has been reintroduced (and improved) to supplement the electrolytic supply of chlorine is the catalysed reaction between oxygen and hydrogen chloride at 400°C.

$$\tfrac{1}{2}O_2 + 2HCl \rightarrow H_2O + Cl_2$$

Bromine and iodine are liberated more readily. The extraction of bromine under relatively mild conditions is described above. Iodine can be displaced from an iodide solution by air. In fact, iodide solutions often turn yellow on standing:

$$2I^-(aq) + \tfrac{1}{2}O_2 + H_2O \rightarrow I_2 + 2OH^-$$

The difference in the ease of oxidation of the halides is also illustrated in their reactions with concentrated sulphuric acid:

$$F^- + H_2SO_4 \rightarrow HF(g) + HSO_4^-$$
$$Cl^- + H_2SO_4 \rightarrow HCl(g) + HSO_4^-$$
$$2Br^- + 2H_2SO_4 \rightarrow Br_2(g) + SO_4^{2-} + SO_2(g) + 2H_2O$$
$$2I^- + 2H_2SO_4 \rightarrow I_2(s) + SO_4^{2-} + SO_2(g) + 2H_2O$$

In the case of the fluorides and chlorides, hydrogen halide is displaced (no change in oxidation state). The bromide and iodide are oxidised to the halogen.

Summary

At the conclusion of this chapter, you should be able to:

1. describe the typical physical and chemical properties of the p-block
   elements, giving suitable examples;
2. define electron affinity;
3. relate the redox properties of the elements to their variable oxidation
   states;
4. compare the elements sulphur and aluminium which are both members
   of the p block;
5. describe the variation in redox properties of the halogens, with examples
   of the application of these properties to their extraction.

Experiments

1. Prepare a non-metal chloride and analyse it (*Nuffield Advanced Science,
   Chemistry,* Longman, 1970).
2. Prepare crystalline $AlCl_3$ from aluminium and hydrochloric acid; compare its chemistry with that of Al_2Cl_6 obtained from aluminium and
   chlorine. Comment on your results.
3. React hydrated aluminium chloride with (*a*) phenolphthalein, (*b*) sodium
   carbonate, (*c*) sodium hydroxide.
4. Investigate and explain the reactions of SO_2 and acidified solutions of (*a*)
   dichromate, (*b*) permanganate, (*c*) iron(II) sulphate, (*d*) copper(I)
   chloride.
5. Examine the effect of chlorine water on solutions of KCl, KI, KBr. What
   happens if tetrachloromethane is also present?
6. Examine the effect of concentrated sulphuric acid on the halides. Repeat
   in the presence of manganese(IV) oxide.
7. Compare the effects of water on a variety of p-block halides.
8. Electrolyse concentrated sodium chloride solution in the presence of
   BDH indicator. Identify the products.
9. Reactions of halogens and halides (*Nuffield Advanced Science, Chemistry;* expt. 5.2).
10. Use of iodine in titrimetry.

References

The experimental values of atomic electron affinities; E. C. M. Chen and
W. E. Wentworth, *J. Chem. Educ.,* 1975, **52,** 186—489.
The extraction of bromine from sea water; B. Haines, Schools Information
Centre on the Chemical Industry, 1975, Bulletin 11, 16—22.
Extraction of bromine from sea water; H. Fossett, *Chem. Ind.,* 1971,
1161—71.
Chlorine; G. D. Twigg, *Sch. Sci. Rev.,* 1966, 375—407.
Chlorine from waste hydrogen chloride, in: *Critical Readings in Chemistry;*
M. G. Brown (Longman, 1965), p. 61.

128 Films

The chemistry of aluminium (Reynolds Metals Co., U.S.A.).
The family of halogens (McGraw-Hill).
Bromine — element from the sea (CHEM Study).
Chlorine (I.C.I.).

Questions

1. What are the products of the following reactions:
   (a) $S + Cl_2$;
   (b) $S + O_2$;
   (c) $S + HNO_3$;
   (d) $S + H_2$?
2. How do the following react with sulphur dioxide:
   (a) water;
   (b) hydrogen sulphide;
   (c) potassium dichromate;
   (d) magnesium;
   (e) potassium permanganate?
3. How do aluminium and sulphur differ in their chemistry?
4. What is meant by 'electron affinity'? Which elements of the p block can be expected to form cations and which will form anions? Give your reasons.
5. How do the halogens vary in their reactions with:
   (a) a d-block metal such as chromium;
   (b) a non-metal such as sulphur;
   (c) a solution of potassium iodide;
   (d) water?
6. How do the potassium halides react with:
   (a) oxygen;
   (b) chlorine;
   (c) concentrated sulphuric acid?
7. Find out the details on the extraction of the halogens from natural sources.

Chapter 11

The d-block elements

An examination of the values of the ionisation energies (Fig. 8.2), electron affinities (Fig. 10.2) and the electronegativities (Table 2.1) of the d-block elements leads to two generalisations:

(a) the values for the d-block elements are intermediate between those of the s- and p-block elements;

(b) the values for the elements in each row of the d-block are fairly similar, the variation across a row being less marked than that in a row of p-block elements.

As a result of factor (a), it is possible to name these as *transition elements*, that is they show a transition in properties from the general properties of the s-block elements to those of the p-block elements. As a result of item (b), the elements are very similar to each other, showing a less pronounced change in properties than that observed for the p-block elements.

Elemental properties

One property of these elements is that they are metallic. We will consider vanadium, chromium, manganese, iron and copper as typical examples. It is natural to compare them to the other block of metals discussed: the s-block metals.

(a) The transition metals are harder and stronger (i.e. they have a greater tensile strength) than the s-block metals. This can be illustrated by the ease with which many of the latter elements can be cut with a pen-knife; this is not so easy with the transition elements. They are nevertheless malleable and ductile like the s-block elements.

(b) The transition metals have melting points which are generally higher than those of the s-block elements (see Fig. 9.2). This has been related to the strength of the binding by the valence electrons (page 111). These elements have more valence electrons than the s-block elements and so the atoms are bound together more strongly.

(c) The metals are less reactive than the s-block metals in the same period. This is a result of the higher ionisation energies; they are more difficult to oxidise. Therefore, for example, they are corroded more slowly by air; water is only slowly reduced by the metals (often only at red heat). Whereas the s-block elements react vigorously with dilute acid (often explosively), the d-block metals react more slowly, even with the concentrated acids.

$$Fe + 2H^+ \rightarrow Fe^{2+} + H_2$$
$$3Fe + 4H_2O \rightarrow Fe_3O_4 + 4H_2$$

They react with non-metals when heated to red heat.
$$Fe + S \rightarrow FeS$$

Compounds

(d) The cations are hydrated due to the attraction between the simple ions and polar water molecules. In this respect, the d-block metals resemble metals of the p block. $[V(H_2O)_6]^{3+}$, $[Cr(H_2O)_6]^{3+}$, $[Mn(H_2O)_6]^{2+}$, $[Fe(H_2O)_6]^{3+}$, $[Cu(H_2O)_6]^{2+}$ occur in dilute aqueous solutions. In the highest oxidation states oxoanions are formed: VO_3^- (vanadate), CrO_4^{2-} (chromate), MnO_4^- (permanganate), FeO_4^{2-} (ferrate), CuO_2^- (cuprate).

(e) The oxides are variable in character. They form weak bases or amphoteric oxides in the lowest oxidation states (V_2O_3, Cr_2O_3, MnO, FeO, CuO) and acidic oxides in the highest states.

(f) In addition to the hydrated salts ((d) above), the elements also form covalent anhydrous chlorides. Whereas the former compounds have typical ionic properties, the latter compounds are volatile, easily sublimed, and readily hydrolysed. (Compare these characteristics with the analogous aluminium compounds, page 124).

Variable oxidation states

As previously mentioned, the elements of the d block can form compounds in which the transition metal displays a variety of oxidation states. Table 11.1 lists the oxidation states of the typical metals.

Table 11.1 Oxidation states of some d metals (the most stable states are underlined)

Oxidation state	Ion	Colour	Oxidation state	Ion	Colour
Vanadium			**Chromium**		
+2	$V(H_2O)_6^{2+}$	violet	+2	$Cr(H_2O)_6^{2+}$	blue
+3	$V(H_2O)_6^{3+}$	green	+3	$Cr(H_2O)_6^{3+}$	violet
+4	VO^{2+}	blue	+4	CrO_4^{4-}	blue-black
+5	VO_3^-	colourless	+5	CrO_4^{3-}	blue
			+6	CrO_4^{2-}	yellow
Manganese			**Iron**		
+2	$Mn(H_2O)_6^{2+}$	pink	+2	$Fe(H_2O)_6^{2+}$	green
+3	$Mn(H_2O)_6^{3+}$	red	+3	$Fe(H_2O)_6^{3+}$	violet
+4	$Mn(H_2O)_6^{4+}$	black	+4	FeO_3^{2-}	black
+5	MnO_4^{3-}	blue	+5	FeO_4^{3-}	black
+6	MnO_4^{2-}	green	+6	FeO_4^{2-}	red-purple
+7	MnO_4^-	purple			
Copper					
+1	$Cu(H_2O)_6^+$	colourless			
+2	$Cu(H_2O)_6^{2+}$	blue			
+3	CuO_2^-	blue-grey			

Many of these states are unstable; usually there are two stable states. As with the p-block elements, this leads to a possibility of redox reactions (page 123). For example Cr^{2+} solutions are strong reducing agents and CrO_4^{2-} is an oxidising agent; both reagents are converted to the Cr^{3+} state in their reactions.

Complex formation

The existence of aqua (water) complexes and oxo complexes has already been mentioned. The d-block metal ions are characterised by the ease with which they form complexes with a large range of ligands. For example, copper ions, Cu^{2+}, can coordinate with water:

$[Cu(H_2O)_4]^{2+}$,

with ammonia:
$[Cu(NH_3)_4]^{2+}$,

with chloride ions:
$[CuCl_4]^{2-}$,

and with cyanide ions:
$[Cu(CN)_4]^{2-}$.

132

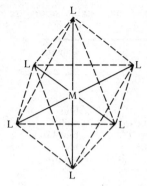

Fig. 11.1 Octahedral shape of a complex ion

The number of groups coordinated to the metal is known as the coordination number.

The complexes of copper can vary from those described; in dilute solution the coordination number may be six rather than four, and sometimes, as with the cyano complex, the lower oxidation state may be more stable, so the product will normally be $[Cu(CN)_4]^{3-}$.

For most cations the coordination number is six. These are described as hexacoordinated or octahedral complexes. The latter term refers to the overall shape of the complex (Fig. 11.1). The oxo ions often have lower coordination numbers, but this is affected by different bonding arrangements.

The nomenclature of these ions has now been systematised to cope with the ever-increasing number of complexes. The name consists of four parts: the number and types of ligand, the element, its oxidation state and the simple cation or anion. This can be illustrated with a few examples.

1. $[Cu(NH_3)_4]^{2+}SO_4^{2-}$: The complex ion is normally enclosed by square brackets in the formula. The complex ion is the cation. In cations the metals retain their normal elemental name, in this case, 'copper'. This is followed, in Roman numerals and enclosed by brackets, by the oxidation state of the central element; 'copper(II)' in this example. This is preceded by the ligand. Ammonia is named 'ammine'; water is 'aqua'; otherwise, generally, neutral ligands retain their molecular name and anionic ligands assume the ending -o (e.g. chloro, cyano). In this case there are four ammonia groups: 'tetrammine' is therefore prefixed to the metal. So, the full name is tetraamminecopper(II) sulphate. Note that the name of the complex ion is continuous; no gaps are introduced between the component parts.

2. $[Fe(H_2O)_6]^{2+}Cl^-_2$: Before continuing with this section, attempt to name this compound.

The central ion, iron, has the oxidation state +2, and there are six water ligands. This name would be hexaaquairon(II) chloride.

3. $K^+_3[Fe(CN)_6]^{3-}$. This ion involves six cyano groups in the anion. The general rule is to add -ate to an elemental form or to replace metallic suffixes (e.g. -ium in aluminium) by the -ate suffix. Hence the names cobaltate, chromate. Some names are not easily adapted to these modifications, for

Table 11.2 Nomenclature of complex oxo ions

Ion	Systematic name	Conventional name
CrO_4^{2-}	tetraoxochromate(VI)	chromate
MnO_4^{2-}	tetraoxomanganate(VI)	manganate(VI)
MnO_4^-	tetraoxomanganate(VII)	permanganate
VO^{2+}	oxovanadium(IV)	vanadyl

example, 'ironate'. These names are, therefore, modified to their former Latin forms: ferrate, cuprate. The name of this compound is potassium hexacyanoferrate(III).

4. $[Co(NH_3)_5Cl]^{2+}Cl^-_2$. When two or more types of ligand are present, the ligands are placed in alphabetical order: ammine then chloro. The prefix mono- is usually omitted. This compound would be named pentaammminechlorocobalt(III) chloride.

The same principle can be applied to oxo ions, but often for convenience the 'oxo' is omitted; sometimes, for historical reasons, the name is modified rather than introducing the oxidation state (see Table 11.2).

Colour

A characteristic feature of the transition metal ions is that they are usually coloured. The colour is related to the oxidation state of the element (see Table 11.1), and also to the nature of the complexing ligand. In Table 11.1, the low oxidation states involve the aqua ligands but these may be replaced by other ligands. The colour changes with a change of ligand:

$[Cu(H_2O)_4]^{2+}$ light blue
$[CuCl_4]^{2-}$ green
$[Cu(NH_3)_4]^{2+}$ dark blue
$[Cu(CN)_4]^{2-}$ colourless.

Similarly, the hexaaquairon(II) ion, $[Fe(H_2O)_6]^{2+}$, is green; the hexacyanoferrate(II) ion is violet. Hexaaquachromium(III) compounds are violet; hexaamminochromium(III) compounds are yellow. Hexaaquavanadium(III) is a green ion, whereas the ammine complex is red-brown in colour. Manganese forms pink aqua complex ions and blue hexacyanomanganate(II) ions.

Paramagnetism

The ability of magnets to attract iron objects is well known. Magnetic properties are also displayed by some transition metal compounds. When suspended in a glass phial between the poles of a strong magnet these compounds are drawn to the magnet. This magnetism, which is much weaker than the ferromagnetism, is known as *paramagnetism*. It has been shown to be related to the number of unpaired electrons in the compounds. The greater the number of unpaired electrons, the larger the degree of paramagnetism in the compound.

The hydrated iron(III) ion has five unpaired electrons:

$$_{26}Fe : \quad 3s^2 \qquad 3p^6 \qquad 3d^6 \qquad 4s^2$$

$$_{26}Fe^{3+} : \quad 3s^2 \qquad 3p^6 \qquad 3d^5$$

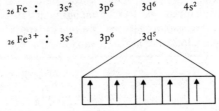

The iron(II) ion has four unpaired electrons:

$$Fe^{2+} : \quad 3s^2 \qquad 3p^6 \qquad 3d^6$$

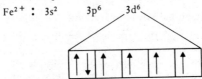

So, iron(III) salts have greater paramagnetic effects than iron(II) salts. Similarly, chromium(II) salts (d^4, 4 unpaired electrons) display stronger effects than chromium(III) compounds (d^3, three unpaired electrons); copper(II) ions (d^9) have stronger degrees of paramagnetism than the copper(I) compounds (d^{10}) with one and zero unpaired electrons respectively. In fact, copper(I) ions display no paramagnetism. Vanadium(II) ions have three unpaired electrons (d^3) and vanadium(III) ions have two unpaired electrons (d^2) so vanadium(II) compounds are the more paramagnetic. Manganese(II) compounds (d^5, five unpaired electrons) are more paramagnetic than manganese(III) compounds (d^4, four unpaired electrons).

The metals of the d block differ from those of the s block in several respects. The distinctive elemental properties have been described (page 129). In their compounds the elements display the following general characteristics:

(a) they form complex ions;
(b) they exist in several oxidation states;
(c) their ions are coloured; and
(d) the ions are paramagnetic.

d-block metals in biological systems

Several of the s-block cations (sodium, potassium, magnesium and calcium) are involved in living organisms and are fairly mobile, moving from one part of the system to another with ease. The d-block metals, in contrast, have generally fixed chemical environments and are most commonly found in proteins.

One of the more important characteristics of transition metals noted in this chapter is that of variable oxidation state and so the ability to undergo oxidation or reduction. This is reflected in several of the biological applications of the metals. For example, manganese occurs in dehydrogenases (enzymes aiding the removal of hydrogen from molecules); iron is the active constituent of haemoglobin, the molecule responsible for the transport of oxygen in the body; copper is found in oxidases (enzymes accelerating oxidation reactions); iron and molybdenum are the active metals in nitrogenase, the enzyme which is active in the natural fixation of nitrogen.

We have also seen (page 131) that the d-block metals form complexes. Natural systems involve these metals in complexes. The necessity for this is illustrated in the case of iron. If oxygen is passed into a solution of an iron(II) salt, the iron is converted to iron(III) which is eventually precipitated as iron(III) hydroxide. This cannot be transported in a fluid state nor does it readily give up its oxygen and return to iron(II). Coordination to a porphyrin unit (page 211) enables the iron to take up oxygen in a form that is both soluble and readily reduced.

The chemical study of the metals in biological systems is still in its infancy because of the difficulty of determining the structure of many of the functional molecules (they are extremely complicated) and the detailed nature of the reactions involved in the cells (only small quantities of the chemicals are in use at any time). The chemistry and biochemistry of these metals is fascinating and undoubtedly includes many aspects awaiting discovery and explanation.

Summary

At the conclusion of this chapter, you should be able to:

1. state why the d-block elements can be described as transition elements;
2. state the typical properties of the metals and contrast them with the s-block metals;
3. give examples of the complex nature of the ions and the variable acid-base character of the oxides;
4. show how the colour of the ions is related to the oxidation state and coordinating ligand in the ion;
5. write the systematic name of a complex compound, given its chemical formula;
6. describe the paramagnetism of d-block ions.

Experiments

1. Investigation of the oxidation numbers of a d-block element, such as vanadium (*Nuffield Advanced Science, Chemistry*; expt. 16.1).
2. Investigation of complexes (ibid., expt. 16.2).

3. Effects of transition metal compounds as catalysts, e.g. the ions in peroxodisulphate–iodide reaction; the oxides in potassium chlorate decomposition.
4. Measurement of paramagnetism by the Gouy balance method.
5. Use of high oxidation state d-block elements (e.g. Mn(VII), Cr(VI)) in titrimetry.
6. General properties of transition metals in their lower oxidation states and in their higher oxidation states.
7. Preparation of complexes, e.g. $K_3[Fe(C_2O_4)_3].3H_2O$.
8. Preparation of metals in uncommon states, e.g. iron(VI) as barium ferrate(VI) and chromium(II) as chromium(II) ethanoate.

References

Heavy metals in biological systems; R. J. P. Williams, *Endeavour,* 1967, 96–100.
Micronutrients; R. J. Taylor (Unilever Educational Booklet, No. 9).
Nitrogenase; R. R. Eady and J. R. Postgate, *Nature,* 1974, **249,** 805–10.
Vanadium in the living world; N. M. Senozan, *J. Chem. Educ.,* 1974, **51,** 503–5.
Hemocyanin, the copper blood; N. M. Senozan, *J. Chem. Educ.,* 1976, **53,** 684–8.
The biochemistry of iron; S. A. Cotton, *Educ. Chem.,* 1976, **13,** 180–3.

Films

Vanadium – a transition element (CHEM Study).

Questions

1. Describe the typical properties of a d-block element, illustrating your answer with a metal of your own choice.
2. Find out how two of the d-block elements are used commercially. To what extent are these applications related to the typical d-block properties? Could an s-block element be used as an alternative in any of these applications?
3. Write systematic names for the following compounds:
   (a) $[Co(NH_3)_6](NO_3)_3$; (b) $K_3[Fe(C_2O_4)_3] \cdot 3H_2O$; (c) NH_4VO_3; (d) $K[Cr(H_2O)_2(C_2O_4)_2]$; (e) $Na_3[Co(NO_2)_6]$.
4. Describe the importance of transition elements in biological systems.

Part 3

Chemical energetics

Chapter 12

Electrochemistry

Conductivity

One of the distinctive characteristics of ionic compounds is that in solution, or when molten, they conduct electricity. In physics it is commonplace to measure the resistance of a compound to the flow of electricity (R measured in ohms). As the resistance decreases, the ability of a material to conduct electricity increases. Similarly, a substance of high resistance is a poor conductor. So, the conductivity, or *conductance* (G), is equal to the reciprocal of the resistance (R), and the units are ohms^{-1} (or siemens).

$$G = \frac{1}{R}$$

The ability of a solution to carry the current between the two electrodes (Fig. 12.1) of a cell is dependent on the distance, l m, between the electrodes and the cross-section, A m^2, of each of the electrodes. The specific conductance, κ (in ohms $^{-1}$m^{-1}), is given by

$$G = \kappa \cdot \frac{A}{l}$$

The conductivity increases as the cross-sectional area increases (there are more particles available to carry the current), and decreases as the path length

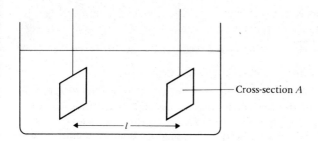

Cross-section A

Fig. 12.1 Dimensions of a conductivity cell

increases (the potential is applied over a greater length and so more work has to be performed to carry the same current). Since it is not possible to measure A/l accurately, the cell is standardised for these terms. The expression A/l is known as the *cell constant*. This is performed by the determination of the conductance of a solution of known specific conductance, usually potassium chloride solution (Table 12.1).

Table 12.1   Specific conductance of KCl(aq)

Concentration (mol 1^{-1})	Specific conductance (ohms^{-1} m^{-1})
1.000	11.17 (298 K)
1.000	9.78 (291 K)
1.000	6.51 (273 K)
0.100	1.29 (298 K)
0.010	0.14 (298 K)
0.001	0.015 (298 K)

For example, the resistance of a cell containing 0.010 0 M KCl solution is found to be 1 223 ohms at 298 K. The same cell has a resistance of 4 546 ohms when it contains a 0.05 M ethanoic acid solution at 298 K. For the first solution,

$$G = \kappa \cdot \frac{A}{l}$$

But, $G = \dfrac{l}{R} = \dfrac{1}{1\ 223} = 8.18 \times 10^{-4}$

So, $8.18 \times 10^{-4} = 0.14 \times \dfrac{A}{l}$

Therefore $\dfrac{A}{l} = 5.84 \times 10^{-3}$

For the ethanoic acid,

$$\kappa = \frac{1}{4\ 546} \times \frac{1}{5.84 \times 10^{-3}}$$

$$= 3.76 \times 10^{-2}\ \text{ohm}^{-1}\ \text{m}^{-1}$$

The basic circuitry for a conductance cell is a Wheatstone Bridge (Fig. 12.2). An a.c. current from an induction coil has to be used to prevent the release of gases by electrolysis. The gases adhere to the electrodes forming a gaseous layer which is a poor electrical conductor. As a result, the current drops and so the applied potential has to be increased in order that the cell reaction may continue. This effect is known as *polarisation.*

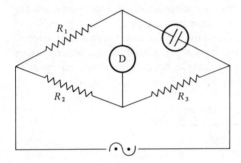

Fig. 12.2   Circuit for conductance cell

The resistances R_1, R_2 and R_3 are adjusted until no current flows through the detector. At this point, the balance point, the resistance of the cell is given by

$$\frac{R(\text{cell})}{R_1} = \frac{R_3}{R_2}$$

so the cell resistance = $R_1 \cdot R_3/R_2$. In order to find the balance point, an a.c. detector must be used. Suitable detectors include earphones, an oscilloscope, a magic eye device or an ammeter with a diode rectifier.

The cell used is usually of a fairly standard form (Fig. 12.3) consisting of two parallel platinum electrodes covered with platinum black. Platinum black electrodes are electrodes with special surface characteristics which minimise polarisation effects.

As is clear from Table 12.1, the conductance varies with concentration. A typical conductivity curve is shown in Fig. 12.4. An increase in concentration produces two counteracting effects:
(a) an increase in the number of molecules and so an increase in the number of ions, the conducting particles; and
(b) a decrease in the degree of ionisation since the number of solvent molecules available for ion formation is less, ions being formed by the interaction of solvent molecules and solute.
The former effect is predominant in the section LM (Fig. 12.4) and (b) is the

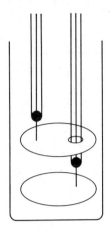

Fig. 12.3   Conductance cell

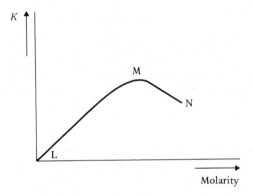

Fig. 12.4   Conductance curve

more significant between M and N. In order to separate these effects, an additional term is used: *molar conductance*. This is defined so that concentration (the number of dissolved particles) is taken into account. Molar conductance (Λ) is measured in units of $ohms^{-1}\ m^2\ mol^{-1}$.

$$\Lambda = \frac{10^{-3} \cdot \kappa}{M} \quad \text{where } M = \text{molarity.}$$

In the example given above (page 139), the molar conductivity of the 0.05 M ethanoic acid would be

$$\Lambda = \frac{10^{-3} \cdot (3.76 \times 10^{-2})}{0.05} = 7.52 \times 10^{-4}\ ohm^{-1}\ m^2\ mol^{-1}$$

Figure 12.5 shows typical curves obtained for the variation of molar conductances with concentration. Electrolytes can be classified into two groups determined by the type of curve obtained. Some electrolytes show

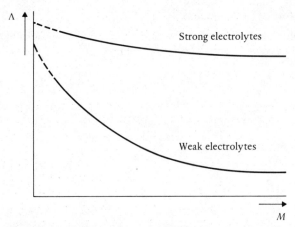

Fig. 12.5 Variation in molar conductance with concentration

little change in their molar conductance with concentration; these are strong electrolytes, i.e. those which are almost completely dissociated into ions in solution. Weak electrolytes show a continually changing degree of dissociation into ions, the extent of the dissociation being dependent on the concentration. The value of the molar conductance at a concentration of zero (or, at 'infinite dilution') Λ_0, corresponds to complete dissociation into ions. So, the percentage dissociation (α) is given by

$$\alpha = \frac{100 \cdot \Lambda}{\Lambda_0}$$

For $0.05\,M$ ethanoic acid, $\Lambda_0 = 3.68 \times 10^{-2}$, at 298 K, so the degree of dissociation into ions is $\dfrac{100 \cdot (7.52 \times 10^{-4})}{3.68 \times 10^{-2}} = 2.04$ per cent.

At infinite dilution (i.e. complete dissociation into ions) the conductance of an electrolyte is determined by the conductance of the constituent ions. These latter values are sometimes called the 'mobilities of the ions' (see Table 12.2).

Table 12.2 Molar conductance at infinite dilution for some common ions at 298 K

Ion	Molar conductance $\times 10^4$ (ohms^{-1} m^2 mol^{-1})
H^+	349.6
NH_4^+	73.6
Na^+	50.1
Li^+	38.7
OH^-	199.1
Cl^-	76.3

$$\Lambda_0 \text{ (electrolyte)} = \Lambda_0 \text{ (cation)} + \Lambda_0 \text{ (anion)}$$

For example, the molar conductances of the sodium and ethanoate ions at infinite dilution are 5.01×10^{-3} and 4.09×10^{-3} $ohms^{-1} m^2 mol^{-1}$ respectively.

So, Λ_0 (salt) = $(5.01 \times 10^{-3}) + (4.09 \times 10^{-3})$.

The value for sodium ethanoate is found independently to be 9.10×10^{-3} $ohms^{-1} m^2 mol^{-1}$. The value for sodium chloride is found to be 1.265×10^{-2} $ohms^{-1} m^2 mol^{-1}$; compare this with the value predicted from Table 12.2.

Conductiometric titrations

The variation in conductance with concentration of ions provides a means of titrimetric analysis. Consider the neutralisation of sodium hydroxide solution by hydrochloric acid. If the cell contains sodium hydroxide solution only, the

$$Na^+(aq) + OH^-(aq) + H^+(aq) + Cl^-(aq) \rightarrow Na^+(aq) + Cl^-(aq) + H_2O$$

conductance is relatively high. As acid is added, the conductivity drops due to the removal of hydroxide ions as covalent water molecules and their replacement with chloride ions which have a lower conductance (see Table 12.2). At the end-point, the conductivity reaches a minimum and increases thereafter due to the build-up of excess hydrogen ions (Fig. 12.6).

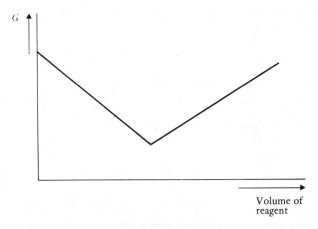

Fig. 12.6 Progress of a conductiometric titration of strong acid with strong base

If a weak alkali is used instead of sodium hydroxide, the conductance is less initially, and the addition of acid increases the conductivity up to the end-point as cations and anions replace the undissociated molecules. After the

$$NH_4OH(aq) + H^+(aq) + Cl^-(aq) \rightarrow NH_4^+(aq) + Cl^-(aq) + H_2O$$

end-point, the conductivity rises more rapidly due to the excess ions of the

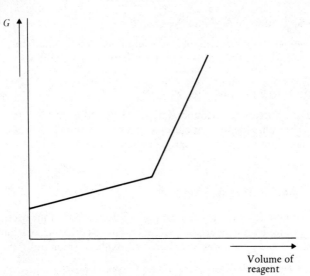

Fig. 12.7 Conductiometric titration of a strong acid with a weak base

strong acid (Fig. 12.7). Table 12.3 gives the molar conductances of some common reagents. From these values it is obvious that in Fig. 12.6 the conductance at the end-point (Na^+Cl^- solution) must be below that of the free acid or base. On the other hand, neutralisation of ammonia solution causes an increase from 9.66 to 122.5 units at 291 K (see Table 12.3), and then to an even higher value due to excess acid.

Table 12.3 Molar conductance of some common reagents

Electrolyte (0.01 M in water)	$\Lambda \times 10^4/ohms^{-1}\ m^2\ mol^{-1}$ 298 K	291 K
HCl	411.8	368.1
NaCl	118.45	102.0
NH_4Cl	141.21	122.5
NaOH	237.9	
CH_3COOH		14.50
NH_4OH		9.66

Electrode potentials

When an element is placed in a solution of its ions, a potential difference occurs between the element and the ions. For example, for a metal there is an equilibrium set up in which there is a balance between the tendency for the

$$M \rightleftharpoons M^{n+} + ne^-$$

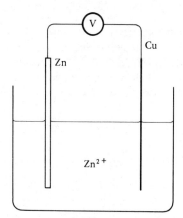

Fig. 12.8 An invalid method for the determination of the electrode potential of zinc

metal to dissolve and the tendency for the ions to be reduced back to the metal. The potential that exists between a metal and a solution of its ions is known as the *electrode potential*.

Unfortunately it is not possible to measure these values direct. For example, if a voltmeter is connected to the metal and the solution through copper wire connections, a new electrode system is set up, a Cu/Zn^{2+} electrode. So the voltmeter will measure the *difference* between the potentials of the Zn/Zn^{2+} and the Cu/Zn^{2+} electrodes. An absolute value would only be possible if it were possible to devise an electrode with a zero potential. It is, therefore, conventional to compare values to some chosen electrode (the hydrogen electrode), which is assigned the arbitrary value of zero.

Reference electrodes

A standard hydrogen electrode system is shown in Fig. 12.9. Hydrogen at

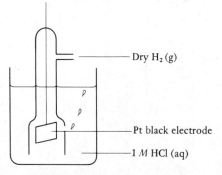

Fig. 12.9 Hydrogen electrode

146   101.3 kPa pressure is passed over a platinum electrode coated with platinum black, and the electrode is dipped into a 1.0 M solution of hydrochloric acid.

This electrode is not easy to set up so other reference electrodes have been designed, being previously standardised against the hydrogen electrode. One such electrode in common use is the calomel electrode, a simple version of which is illustrated in Fig. 12.10. This is standardised as −0.242 V.

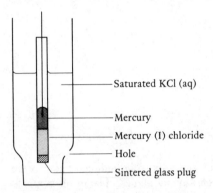

Saturated KCl (aq)

Mercury

Mercury (I) chloride

Hole

Sintered glass plug

Fig. 12.10   The calomel electrode

Standard electrode potentials

In order to determine an electrode potential it is necessary to connect the electrode under consideration to the reference electrode without introducing another electrode. If a metal wire is used to connect the electrolyte solutions, then two new electrodes are introduced (see Fig. 12.8). The connection is made through a 'salt bridge'. The salt bridge consists of a saturated solution of potassium chloride in agar-agar jelly (Fig. 12.11). The salt bridge is used because it is a conducting medium which does not contaminate the electrode (so affecting its potential) and it does not introduce new electrode systems.

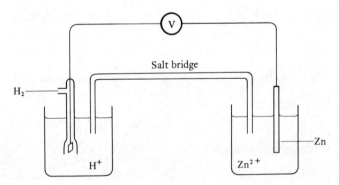

Salt bridge

H_2

H^+

Zn^{2+}

Zn

Fig. 12.11   Apparatus for the determination of the electrode potential of zinc

Table 12.4   Some standard electrode potentials

Electrode	$E_{298}^{\ominus}$/volts
Pt,Na(Hg) | Na$^+$(aq,1 M)	−2.71
Zn | Zn^{2+}(aq,1 M)	−0.76
Pt,H$_2$(101.3 kPa) | H$_3$O$^+$(1 M,aq)	0.00
Ag,AgCl | Cl$^-$(aq,1 M)	+0.22
Pt,Hg,Hg$_2$Cl$_2$ | Cl$^-$(aq,1 M)	+0.27
Cu | Cu^{2+}(aq,1 M)	+0.34
Pt,Cl$_2$(101.3 kPa) | Cl$^-$(aq,1 M)	+1.36

The e.m.f. of the cell gives the numerical value of the electrode potential; by convention, the sign (+ or −) of the electrode is determined by the polarity of the electrode with respect to a hydrogen electrode. For example, a zinc electrode is negative with respect to a hydrogen electrode, with an e.m.f. of 0.76 V for the cell. So, the electrode potential for zinc is −0.76 V. Conversely, copper has an electrode potential of +0.34 V. Table 12.4 gives a list of some electrode potentials. It is found that the electrode potential is dependent on concentration and temperature, so it is normal to quote a *standard electrode potential*. This is the value for a 1 M solution of the ions at 25°C (298 K). Gases must be at standard atmospheric pressure (101.3 kPa). The standard potential is represented as $E^{\ominus}$. So, $E_{298}^{\ominus}$ (Zn^{2+}/Zn) = −0.76 V (see below for an explanation of this formulation).

It is convenient to describe a cell in a short-hand form. For example, the cell in Fig. 12.11 is written as

Pt, H$_2$(101.3 kPa) \| H$_3$O$^+$ (aq.,1 M) ‖ Zn^{2+}(aq.,1 M) \| Zn

The hydrogen electrode is always written on the left so that the sign of the electrode potential represents the sign of the right hand electrode. The electrode potential is, therefore, written in the form $E^{\ominus}$(Zn^{2+}/Zn) to represent this half-cell; since this represents reduction (Zn^{2+} → Zn), these potentials are also called *reduction potentials*. The electrodes are separated from the solutions by a vertical line and solution junctions are indicated by double vertical lines. The components of an electrode (e.g. Pt and H$_2$) or a solution are separated by commas.

A metal with a negative potential is one that is more readily oxidised than is hydrogen. For example, since zinc has a value of −0.76 V, it experiences the change

Zn → Zn^{2+} + 2e^-

more readily than hydrogen's change

½H$_2$ → H$^+$ + e^-

The negative electrode is the one at which oxidation occurs; the positive electrode is a system which undergoes reduction.

Table 12.5   Electrochemical series

Electrode system	$E^{\ominus}_{298\ K}$/volts
$Li^+(aq)/Li(s)$	-3.03
$K^+(aq)/K(s)$	-2.92
$Ca^{2+}(aq)/Ca(s)$	-2.87
$Na^+(aq)/Na(s)$	-2.71
$Mg^{2+}(aq)/Mg(s)$	-2.37
$Al^{3+}(aq)/Al(s)$	-1.66
$Mn^{2+}(aq)/Mn(s)$	-1.19
$Zn^{2+}(aq)/Zn(s)$	-0.76
$Cr^{3+}(aq)/Cr(s)$	-0.74
$Fe^{2+}(aq)/Fe(s)$	-0.44
$Ni^{2+}(aq)/Ni(s)$	-0.25
$Sn^{2+}(aq)/Sn(s)$	-0.14
$Pb^{2+}(aq)/\ Pb(s)$	-0.13
$2H^+(aq)/H_2(g),\ Pt(s)$	0.00
$Cu^{2+}(aq),\ Cu^+(aq)/Pt(s)$	$+0.15$
$Cu^{2+}(aq)/Cu(s)$	$+0.34$
$O_2(g),\ 4OH^-(aq)/Pt(s)$	$+0.40$
$I_2(aq),\ 2I^-(aq)/Pt(s)$	$+0.54$
$Fe^{3+}(aq),\ Fe^{2+}(aq)/Pt(s)$	$+0.77$
$Ag^+(aq)/Ag(s)$	$+0.80$
$Br_2(aq),\ 2Br^-(aq)/Pt(s)$	$+1.09$
$Cr_2O_7^{2-}(aq),\ Cr^{3+}(aq)/Pt(s)$	$+1.33$
$Cl_2(aq),\ Cl^-(aq)/Pt(s)$	$+1.36$
$H_2O_2 + 2H^+(aq),\ 2H_2O/Pt(s)$	$+1.77$
$F_2(g) + 2H^+(aq),\ 2HF(aq)/Pt(s)$	$+3.06$

So, if the electrode systems are arranged in order of increasing electrode potential (Table 12.5), we have a series which gives us a measure of chemical reactivity, the *electrochemical series*.

Electrochemical series

The higher the position of an element in the electrochemical series, the more likely it is to undergo oxidation (compare zinc and hydrogen in the example given above). If zinc is placed in an aqueous solution of hydrogen ions, zinc undergoes oxidation and hydrogen ions are reduced. That is zinc displaces hydrogen from a solution of its ions:

$$Zn + 2H^+(aq) \rightarrow Zn^{2+}(aq) + H_2$$

This table can be used to determine the likelihood of a chemical reaction occurring. For example, applying the principles described for the zinc/

hydrogen reaction, determine whether lead would displace silver from a solution of its ions.

The electrode potentials are $E^{\ominus}_{298\,K}(Pb^{2+}(aq)/Pb)$ = -0.13 V and $E^{\ominus}_{298\,K}(Ag^+(aq)/Ag)$ = $+0.80$ V. The lead is, therefore, more easily oxidised to lead ions than silver is to silver ions. Also, silver ions are more readily reduced to silver than are lead ions to lead. The preferred changes are:

$Pb \rightarrow Pb^{2+}(aq) + 2e^-$

$Ag^+(aq) + e^- \rightarrow Ag.$

So, the reaction

$Pb + 2Ag^+(aq) \rightarrow Pb^{2+}(aq) + 2Ag$

will probably occur.

It should be emphasised that we can predict only the feasibility of a reaction. There is no guarantee that the reaction will occur on mixing the relevant solutions. Other factors need to be considered, for example, concentration effects (see page 150) and rates of reaction.

Cells

Consider a Daniell cell (Zn and Cu electrode systems) using $1\,M$ solutions; $Cu \mid Cu^{2+}(aq, 1\,M) \parallel Zn^{2+}(aq, 1\,M) \mid Zn$. The standard electrode potentials are $E^{\ominus}(Zn^{2+}/Zn) = -0.76$ V and $E^{\ominus}(Cu^{2+}/Cu) = +0.34$ V

The zinc undergoes oxidation; reduction occurs at the copper electrode. The e.m.f. of the cell is the difference between the two values, since the zinc electrode has a potential 0.76 V below that of the hydrogen electrode and copper is 0.34 V above it.

$+0.34 -(-0.76) = +1.10$ V (see Fig. 12.13)

The overall reaction is the sum of the half-cell reactions:

$Zn \rightarrow Zn^{2+} + 2e^-$

$Cu^{2+} + 2e^- \rightarrow Cu$

$Zn + Cu^{2+} \rightarrow Zn^{2+} + Cu$

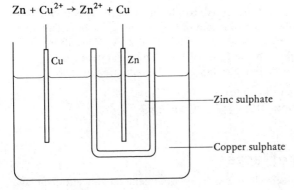

Fig. 12.12   Daniell cell

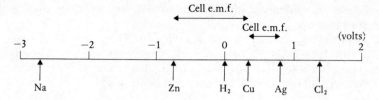

Fig. 12.13   Chart for the determination of cell e.m.f.

The zinc electrode is the negative electrode.

What would be the e.m.f. of a silver–copper cell? The silver electrode ($E^{\ominus}$, +0.80 V) is more positive than the copper electrode ($E^{\ominus}$, +0.34 V) and so reduction must occur at this silver electrode:

$$Ag^+ + e^- \rightarrow Ag$$

At the copper electrode, the change is oxidation:

$$Cu \rightarrow Cu^{2+} + 2e^-$$

The difference between the potentials, the cell e.m.f., is

$$0.80 - 0.34 = 0.46 \text{ V (Fig. 12.13)}$$

The silver electrode is the positive electrode.

Some elements have more than one oxidation state. For example, iron can exist as iron(II) are iron(III) ions. A change in oxidation state can also be represented as an electrode process:

$$Fe^{2+}(aq) \rightarrow Fe^{3+}(aq) + e^-$$

The standard electrode system for such a change is

$$Pt \mid Fe^{2+}(aq, 1\,M), Fe^{3+}(aq, 1\,M)$$

and the standard electrode potential for the system is +0.77 V.

Consider the cell

$$Pt \mid Fe^{2+}(aq, 1\,M), Fe^{3+}(aq, 1\,M \parallel Cl^-(aq, 1\,M) \mid Hg_2Cl_2, Hg, Pt.$$

The e.m.f. of this cell will be equal to the difference in the electrode potentials of the $Fe^{2+}-Fe^{3+}$ electrode and of the calomel electrode. The latter electrode has the standard electrode potential of +0.27 V. The difference in the potentials, and so the cell e.m.f., is 0.50 V. The iron system has the more positive value and so is more likely to represent the reduction process:

positive electrode reaction: $Fe^{3+}(aq) + e^- \rightarrow Fe^{2+}(aq)$
negative electrode reaction: $2Hg + 2Cl^- \rightarrow Hg_2Cl_2 + 2e^-$

Concentration effects

It was noted that the electrode potential is dependent on concentration and temperature. The standard value, $E^{\ominus}$, is given at 298 K for 1 M concentra-

$$E = E^{\ominus} + \frac{2.3RT}{nF} \log_{10}(M_{\text{oxid}})$$

where n is the number of electrons transferred per mole of the ion and M_{oxid} is the molarity of the metal ions.

The change in electrode potentials with concentration allows the production of a cell based solely on this effect. Consider two copper electrodes, one using $0.01\,M$ $CuSO_4(aq)$ and the other $1\,M$ $CuSO_4(aq)$. The standard electrode potential ($1\,M$ $Cu^{2+}(aq)$) is +0.34 V. The value for the lower concentration electrode is given by

$$E = 0.34 + \left(\frac{2.3 \times 8.314 \times 298}{2 \times 96\,487}\right)\log 0.01$$

$$= 0.34 - 0.06$$

$$= 0.28\text{ V}$$

So, the cell e.m.f. is $0.34 - 0.28 = 0.06$ V

In general, for a reaction of the form

$$RED \rightleftharpoons OXID + n\,e^-$$

(where RED, OXID represent the oxidised and reduced forms),

$$E = E^{\ominus} + \frac{2.3RT}{nF} \log_{10}\left(\frac{M_{\text{oxid}}}{M_{\text{red}}}\right)$$

This is known as the Nernst equation. So, for a chlorine electrode

$$Pt,Cl_2(101.3\text{ kPa}) \mid Cl^-(aq)$$

the expression becomes

$$E = E^{\ominus} - \frac{2.3RT}{nF} \log M_{Cl^-}$$

since the active ion is in the reduced form. The chlorine gas is in the standard form and at standard pressure and so will not cause any change in the e.m.f.

For the iron(II)–iron(III) electrode system, $E^{\ominus} = +0.77$ V. When $M_{Fe^{2+}} = 0.50$ and $M_{Fe^{3+}} = 0.05$, then

$$E = 0.77 + \frac{2.3 \times 8.314 \times 298}{1 \times 96\,487} \log_{10}\frac{0.05}{0.50}$$

$$= 0.77 - 0.06$$

$$= 0.71\text{ V}$$

The calomel electrode has a standard electrode potential of +0.28 V. What is its potential for KCl concentration of $0.1\,M$, and for the saturated solution ($4.7\,M$) at 298 K?

The expression for the potential is given above (the chlorine electrode) but the standard potential is 0.27 V (a mercury(I) chloride system is used instead of chlorine gas). For $0.1\,M$ KCl(aq),

$$E = 0.27 - \frac{2.3 \times 8.314 \times 298}{1 \times 96\,487} \log 0.1$$

$$= 0.27 + 0.06$$

$$= 0.33 \text{ V}$$

and for the saturated solution of KCl,

$$E = 0.27 - \left(\frac{2.3 \times 8.314 \times 298}{1 \times 96\,847} \right) \log_{10} 4.7$$

$$= 0.27 - 0.04$$

$$= 0.23 \text{ V}$$

Before proceeding further, determine the potential of a cell based on the zinc and chlorine electrode systems with the zinc ion concentration at $0.10\,M$ and the chloride ion concentration at $0.20\,M$; temperature 298 K.

The cell description is

$$\text{Zn} \mid \text{Zn}^{2+}(\text{aq}, 0.10\,M) \parallel \text{Cl}^-(\text{aq}, 0.20\,M) \mid \text{Cl}_2(101.3 \text{ kPa}), \text{Pt}$$

The standard electrode potentials (Table 12.4) are adjusted to the specified conditions:

$$E_{\text{Zn}^{2+}/\text{Zn}} = -0.76 + \left(\frac{2.3 \times 8.314 \times 298}{2 \times 96\,487} \right) \log 0.1$$

$$= -0.76 - 0.03$$

$$= -0.79 \text{ V}$$

$$E_{\text{Cl}_2/\text{Cl}^-} = +1.36 - \left(\frac{2.3 \times 8.314 \times 298}{1 \times 96\,487} \right) \log 0.2$$

$$= +1.36 + 0.04$$

$$= +1.40 \text{ V}$$

The cell e.m.f. is $(1.40 + 0.79) = 2.19$ V. The chlorine electrode is positively charged.

Potentiometric titration

The variation in potential of a cell with a change in concentration of the electrolytes provides another means of titration. Consider the titration of sodium hydroxide solution with hydrochloric acid. Figure 12.14 illustrates the change in e.m.f. with the volume of added alkali. The end-point is the mid-point of the almost vertical line (that is at the point of inflection). Figure 12.15 shows a similar pattern for ethanoic acid.

It is often difficult to determine exactly the position of the end-point. This can be done with a high degree of confidence using the 'first differential curve'. This is a mathematical concept which indicates that $\Delta E / \Delta V$ is a maximum at a point of inflexion. $\Delta E / \Delta V$ is the gradient of a graph of E (e.m.f.) against V (volume). The method of determination is indicated in Table 12.6 for a titration between iron(II) ions and permanganate ions.

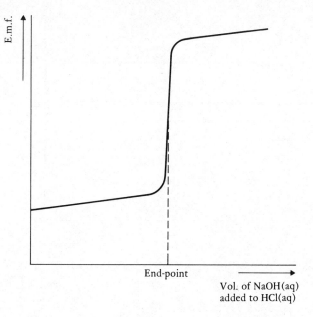

Fig. 12.14 Potentiometric titration of HCl and NaOH

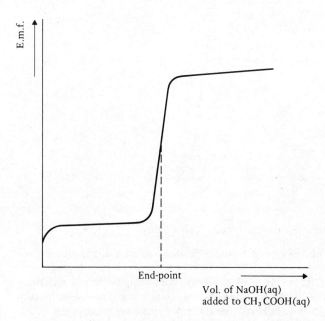

Fig. 12.15 Potentiometric titration of ethanoic acid and sodium hydroxide

154

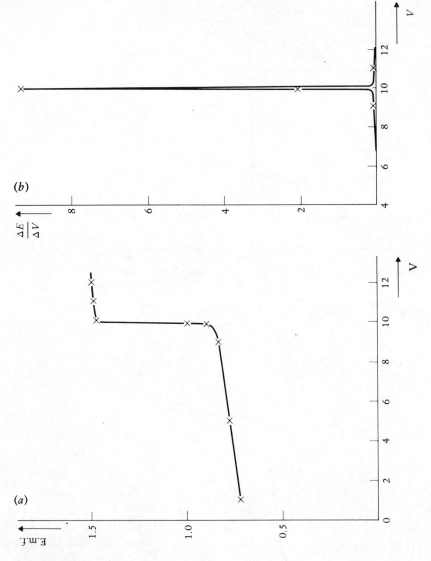

Fig. 12.16 Potentiometric titration (see Table 12.6)

Figures 12.16(a) and (b) give the e.m.f.–volume and first differential curves for this experiment.

The electrometric methods of titration (conductiometric and potentio-metric) are of particular value when the end-points are not easy to detect using the usual visual indicators, for example, in weak acid–weak alkali titrations, in which the pH change at the end-point is too small with respect to the volume additions, and in titrations using strongly coloured solutions,

Table 12.6 Results from a potentiometric titration

Vol. of KMnO₄ (cm³)	E.m.f. (volts)	Increase in e.m.f., ΔE	Increase in vol., ΔV	$\dfrac{\Delta E}{\Delta V}$
1.0	0.726	–	–	–
5.0	0.782	0.056	4.0	0.014
9.0	0.839	0.057	4.0	0.014
9.9	0.899	0.060	0.9	0.067
9.95	1.0	0.101	0.05	2.02
10.0	1.468	0.468	0.05	9.36
10.1	1.485	0.017	0.1	0.17
11.0	1.497	0.012	0.9	0.013
12.0	1.501	0.004	1.0	0.004

which mask changes in the indicator colours. (An elementary, qualitative knowledge of pH is assumed from the TEC level 1 studies. A quantitative discussion is introduced on page 178.)

pH meters

A pH meter gives a direct reading on a meter of the pH of a solution. The principle of pH meters is the same as that for potentiometric titrations. The e.m.f. generated in a solution between the pair of electrodes of a pH meter is related to the hydrogen ion concentration. The use of a hydrogen electrode would be an obvious choice except for its experimental awkwardness. This can be overcome by the use of a *glass electrode* (Fig. 12.17):

Pt, Ag, AgCl | HCl(aq, 0.1 M)

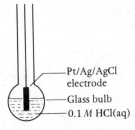

Pt/Ag/AgCl electrode
Glass bulb
0.1 M HCl(aq)

Fig. 12.17 Glass electrode

The platinum wire is plated with silver and then coated with silver chloride; the glass is selectively permeable to hydrogen ions. As a reference electrode, the calomel cell is used. The pH meter measures the e.m.f. of the cell (Fig. 12.18). The scale is usually calibrated to measure pH values where

$$pH = -\log_{10} M_{H^+},$$

and so the pH is proportional to the e.m.f., E.

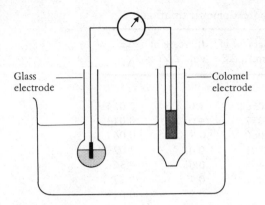

Fig. 12.18 Simplified diagram of the cell of a pH meter

Energy equivalent

The e.m.f. of a cell is defined as the potential under which the cell will do the maximum amount of work. It is the potential when there is no load on the cell.

The work equivalent to this potential is $(e \times E)$ joules, where e is the electronic charge $(1.602 \times 10^{-19}C)$. For a mole of electrons, the energy is $N_0 \cdot e \cdot E$ joules. The quantity $N_0 \cdot e$ C mol^{-1} is known as the Faraday, F ($1F = 96\,487$ C mol^{-1}). So, if n moles of electrons are transferred per mole of the ion, then the energy $= n \cdot E \cdot F$ J mol^{-1}. The energy equivalent to the e.m.f., often called the *free energy change* (ΔG), is given by

$$\Delta G = -n \cdot E \cdot F$$

The symbol Δ, *delta*, used here and in other chapters indicates a change in a term. The negative sign is introduced, by convention, to indicate that energy is *lost* by the cell in doing work (see page 12).

So, in the zinc-chlorine cell, where $E = 2.19$ V (see page 152),

$$\Delta G = -2 \times 2.19 \times 96\,487 \text{ J mol}^{-1}$$
$$= -4.23 \times 10^5 \text{ J mol}^{-1} \text{ or } -423 \text{ kJ mol}^{-1}$$

Similarly, the concentration cell described on page 151 will have the energy equivalent of $-2 \times 0.06 \times 96\,487$ J mol$^{-1} = -11.6$ kJ mol^{-1}.

Now determine the energy equivalent of the copper–zinc cell on page 149).

The e.m.f. was found to be 1.10 V; so the energy equivalent, ΔG, is given by

$$\Delta G = -2 \times 1.10 \times 96\,487 \text{ J mol}^{-1}$$
$$= -212 \text{ kJ mol}^{-1}$$

Summary

At the conclusion of this chapter, you should be able to:

1. state that the conductance of a solution is the reciprocal of its resistance;
2. define the specific conductance of a solution;
3. describe the experimental method for the determination of the cell constant;
4. state why an a.c. supply must be used in the determination of the cell constant;
5. relate the specific and molar conductances of a solute to the concentration;
6. state that the molar conductance at infinite dilution is equal to the molar conductance of the constituent ions;
7. describe the relationship of the molar conductance to the percentage dissociation into ions;
8. describe the progress of a conductiometric titration;
9. describe the meaning of the term electrode potential;
10. describe the construction of the hydrogen and calomel electrodes;
11. describe the procedure for the determination of a standard electrode potential;
12. know that standard electrode potentials are also called reduction potentials;
13. calculate the e.m.f. of a cell from the electrode potentials;
14. determine the charge on the electrodes of a cell;
15. state the Nernst equation and apply it to the calculation of electrode potentials at other concentrations;
16. state that the electrochemical series is a table of electrode systems arranged in order of increasing electrode potential;
17. predict the feasibility of a reaction between two species from their positions in the electrochemical series;
18. state the limitations of the electrochemical series in the prediction of chemical reactivity;
19. describe the progress of a potentiometric titration;
20. determine the first differential curve;
21. describe the structure of a glass electrode and of a pH meter;
22. calculate the energy equivalent of the cell e.m.f.

Experiments

1. *Selected Experiments in Physical Science;* D. H. Marrow (Longman, 1974), Chapter 13: measurement of conductivity, conductivity titrations, use of a direct reading pH meter, potentiometric titrations.
2. *Nuffield Advanced Science, Chemistry* (Longman, 1970), topic 15: some simple redox reactions, measurement of the e.m.f. of some voltaic cells, effect of changes in silver ion concentration on the potential of the $Ag^+(aq)/Ag(s)$ electrode, use of e.m.f. measurements to estimate small

concentrations of ions, measurement of the redox potentials for the $Fe^{3+}(aq)/Fe^{2+}(aq)$ equilibrium and the $2I^-(aq)/I_2(aq)$ equilibrium.

References

Elementary Electrochemistry; A. R. Denaro (Butterworth, 1965).
Electrometric Methods; D. R. Browning (McGraw-Hill, 1969).
Modern Analytical Methods; D. Betteridge and W. E. Hallam (Royal Institute of Chemistry, 1972), Chapter 6.

Films

Electrochemical cells (CHEM Study).
Electromotive force series (McGraw-Hill).
Corrosion in action (3 parts) (International Nickel Co.).

Filmloop

Electrode potentials (Longman).

Questions

1. Describe how you would determine experimentally the conductance of a solution.
    A cell containing a $0.100\,M$ solution of a salt has a resistance of 192 ohms at 291 K. When the cell is filled with $0.02\,M$ KCl(aq) at the same temperature, the resistance is 620 ohms. The molar conductivity of the salt at zero concentration (infinite dilution) is 95.2×10^{-4} ohm^{-1} m^2 mol^{-1}. Calculate the cell constant, the specific and molar conductivities of the salt and its degree of dissociation into ions. (The specific conductivity of $0.02\,M$ KCl(aq) and 291 K is 0.242 ohms^{-1} m^{-1}.)

2. A solution of sodium bromide (25 cm^3) was titrated against $0.45\,M$ silver nitrate solution and the titration was followed using a conductance bridge. The results were as shown in the table (page 159). Plot a graph of the results and calculate the molarity of the sodium bromide solution.

3. Describe how you would determine the standard electrode potential of silver at ambient temperatures.
    Using the values listed in Table 12.5, calculate the e.m.f. of the following cells, stating which electrode is positively charged. All systems are in the standard conditions.
    (a) $Sn(s) \mid Sn^{2+}(aq) \parallel Ag^+(aq) \mid Ag(s)$
    (b) $Pt(s) \mid Cr^{3+}(aq), Cr_2O_7^{2-}(aq) \parallel Cr^{3+}(aq) \mid Cr(s)$
    (c) $Cr(s) \mid Cr^{3+}(aq) \parallel Mn^{2+}(aq) \mid Mn(s)$

Volume of AgNO$_3$ solution added/cm^3	Conductance/10^{-6} ohm^{-1}
0.0	393
1.0	352
2.0	312
3.0	272
4.0	231
5.0	218
6.0	235
7.0	252
8.0	269
9.0	286

    (d) Pt(s), H$_2$(g) | H$^+$(aq) ‖ OH$^-$(aq) | O$_2$(g), Pt(s)
    (e) Zn(s) | Zn^{2+}(aq) ‖ Ag$^+$(aq) | Ag(s)

4. For the cells listed in question 3, indicate the net cell reactions.
5. Calculate the e.m.f. of the cell

    Cr(s) | Cr^{3+}(aq., 0.1 M) ‖ Ni^{2+}(aq., 0.5 M) | Ni(s) at 298 K.

6. The following table gives the results obtained in a potentiometric titration of 10.0 cm^3 hydrochloric acid against 0.100 M sodium hydroxide solution. Plot a graph of the e.m.f. against the volume of alkali and the first derivative curve. Calculate the molarity of the acid.

Volume of alkali/cm^3	e.m.f./V
0.0	0.100
2.0	0.120
4.0	0.140
6.0	0.160
7.0	0.180
8.0	0.280
8.2	0.400
8.4	0.600
8.5	0.800
8.6	0.940
8.8	1.060
9.0	1.070
11.0	1.110
12.0	1.120

7. For each of the cells in questions 3 and 5, determine the free energy change for the cell reaction.

Chapter 13

Energy changes

Energy changes can be recognised in various forms. For example, in Chapter 12 we studied the electrochemistry of cells and related the e.m.f. values of cells to energy changes ('free energy'). This energy can be used to do electrical work. Energy is also recognised as heat energy — heat is radiated from a burning gas or from an electric hotplate. Light is a form of energy — it can excite electrons (page 12) or even break chemical bonds as in the photodegradation (destruction by light) of plastics or dyestuffs. Mechanical energy is recognised by the effort required to lift a load. That sound is a form of energy is apparent by its effect on the eardrums. More recently we have come to recognise the existence of atomic energy changes — both in nuclear power stations and in nuclear bombs.

These energy types are interconvertible: for example, electrical energy can do mechanical work by driving a motor; atomic energy changes can produce electricity (and so heat) or light, heat and sound (in an explosion); photoelectric cells convert light to electrical energy; amplifiers transform electrical pulses into sound energy; thermocouples change heat energy differences into electrical energy. Energy changes are measured in joules.

As shown in the previous chapter, the chemical energy of an ionic reaction can be converted to the electrical energy of a cell. In many reactions, the chemical change is accompanied by the absorption or evolution of heat (discussed further in this chapter); this heat energy arises from changes in the chemical energy of the system. In photosynthesis, the chlorophyll of green plants is able to assist the conversion of light energy from the sun into chemical energy required for the synthesis of sugars from carbon dioxide and water.

Chemical energy is the energy released in a chemical reaction.

While the energy release can be measured (see later), the internal energy (i.e. the energy possessed by the system under given conditions) cannot be determined. When a substance undergoes a change (for example, in a chemical reaction), it is only possible to measure the change in internal energy. The internal energy of a substance is of two forms:

(a) kinetic energy − energy which is due to the translational motion of the molecules, the rotational energy as the molecules turn about their centre of gravity and the vibrational energy of the atoms in the molecules;

(b) potential energy − energy which is due to the attractive forces between molecules and to the chemical bond energies. These energy values are dependent on the positions of the atoms relative to each other.

The sub-atomic particles also have energies in these two categories. The energy change observed in a chemical reaction is due to changes in the internal energies of the molecules. Usually the largest component is the change in bond energies.

Bond energies

When two atoms are brought together in order to form a chemical bond, energy is released due to the attractive forces set up between the nuclei and the electrons. For example, when two hydrogen atoms form a covalent bond, there is a release of 436 kJ mol^{-1}

$$H + H \rightarrow H_2$$

that is for every mole of hydrogen molecules formed 436 kJ of energy are released.

Similarly, on average, the bond energy of the carbon–hydrogen bond formed in hydrocarbons is 416 kJ mol^{-1}. It is experimentally difficult to measure the energy release on forming bonds from elements, so it is more usual to determine the energy required to break the bond, which will be of the same magnitude. Table 13.1 gives some standard bond energies; where a bond (such as C —H above) occurs in several different compounds, the average value is given.

Chemical energy changes

The change in internal energy is given the symbol ΔU. This energy can be displayed as heat changes and physical work. The physical work is represented by expansion (unless the system is forced to remain at constant volume, and then an increase in pressure is observed). This expansion term, in

Table 13.1 Bond energies (values for heteronuclear bonds are average values for such bonds)

Molecule	Bond energy/ kJ mol^{-1}	Bond	Bond energy/ kJ mol^{-1}
F_2	155	C—H	416
Cl_2	246	C—C	346
Br_2	193	C═C	608
I_2	151	C≡C	820
N_2	949	C—F	485
O_2	499	C—Cl	338
H_2	436	C—Br	284
HF	566	C—I	213
HCl	432	C—O	357
HBr	366	C═O	744
HI	299	N—H	392
CO	1075	O—H	466

a system at constant temperature, is only significant if a gas is evolved and it is then equal to 2.48 kJ mol^{-1} of gas produced at 298 K.

This can be summarised as

$$\Delta U = \Delta H - w$$

where ΔH is the change in *enthalpy* and w is the work done by the system. The enthalpy change in a system is the change in energy that occurs when it undergoes a change in its physical or chemical condition. Provided the pressure is constant, the enthalpy change is equal to the heat change in a chemical reaction. If heat is absorbed by the system and work is done by the system, then ΔU represents the net gain in the internal energy by the system. If no gas is evolved (so $w = 0$), then

$$\Delta U = \Delta H$$

If energy is gained by the system then it is given a positive sign; energy lost is negative.

Reactions in which heat energy is released, that is lost to the surroundings, are described as *exothermic* reactions. If heat is absorbed by the reaction, then it is described as an *endothermic* reaction. In an exothermic reaction the temperature of the mixture rises; it drops back to its original temperature as the heat is lost to the surroundings. Initially the temperature of an endothermic reaction drops until the system is able to gain heat from the surroundings. The heat required for the chemical change is absorbed initially from the kinetic energy of the solvent molecules. Since the temperature of a substance is related to the kinetic energy of its particles, the temperature of the solution drops when it loses kinetic energy.

Enthalpy diagrams can be drawn for chemical reactions (Fig. 13.1). In an exothermic reaction (Fig. 13.1(a)), the enthalpy of the products is less than

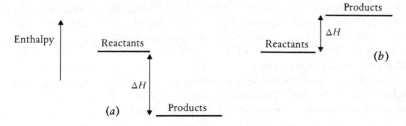

Fig. 13.1 Enthalpy diagrams for chemical reactions

the enthalpy of the reactants. In proceeding from reactants to products, this extra energy must be released. Similarly, when the products have an enthalpy which is greater than that of the reactants, the energy profile is as shown in Fig. 13.1(*b*).

It should be noted, however, that we are describing only the energies of the initial reactants and final products. Most reactions have an intermediate species and their energies would have to be considered in a full energy profile.

Types of enthalpy change

When heat is given out by a chemical system, it is detected and measured by a temperature change (ΔT). The enthalpy change, ΔH, is given by

$\Delta H = -m \cdot s \cdot \Delta T$ where m = mass of material/mol
s = specific heat/J $\deg^{-1}$ mol^{-1}

(ΔT is negative for a temperature drop).

The enthalpy change for a reaction can be measured by conducting the reaction in an insulated calorimeter or vacuum flask (Fig. 13.2). For example, in the reaction between zinc and a solution of a copper salt, it is found that the enthalpy change is -209.8 kJ mol^{-1} at 298 K.

$Zn + Cu^{2+}(aq) \rightarrow Cu + Zn^{2+}(aq)$, $\Delta H = -209.8$ kJ mol^{-1}

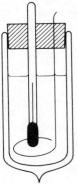

Fig. 13.2   Apparatus for measurement of enthalpy changes

This is known as the *enthalpy of reaction:* the enthalpy change when one mole of a substance undergoes the specified reaction at a stated temperature and pressure. Insulation is essential to prevent uncontrolled loss of heat. It is necessary to keep an account of all heat changes in order to compute the enthalpy change in a reaction.

Certain reactions are usefully classified as special cases. For example, the *enthalpy of neutralisation* is the enthalpy change when one mole of acid is exactly neutralised by base at a stated temperature and pressure:

$$Na^+(aq) + OH^-(aq) + H^+(aq) + Cl^-(aq) \rightarrow Na^+(aq) + Cl^-(aq) + H_2O$$
$$\Delta H = -57.3 \text{ kJ mol}^{-1} \text{ at } 291K$$

An examination of this reaction shows that the net change is

$$OH^-(aq) + H^+(aq) \rightarrow H_2O$$

This implies that the enthalpy change for this reaction is 57.3 kJ mol^{-1}. Reactions between other strong acids and bases reduce to the same equation. Are their enthalpies of neutralisation also approximately $-57.3 \text{ kJ mol}^{-1}$?

$$H^+(aq) + NO_3^-(aq) + Na^+(aq) + OH^-(aq) \rightarrow Na^+(aq) + NO_3^- + H_2O$$
$$\Delta H = -57.2 \text{ kJ mol}^{-1} \text{ at } 291 \text{ K}$$
$$H^+(aq) + Cl^-(aq) + K^+(aq) + OH^-(aq) \rightarrow K^+(aq) + Cl^-(aq) + H_2O$$
$$\Delta H = -57.2 \text{ kJ mol}^{-1} \text{ at } 291 \text{ K}$$

The quantity of heat released when a weak acid or base is used is smaller; energy is absorbed in the dissociation of molecules into ions.

$$H^+(aq) + Cl^-(aq) + NH_4OH(aq) \rightarrow NH_4^+(aq) + Cl^-(aq) + H_2O$$
$$\Delta H = -51.3 \text{ kJ mol}^{-1} \text{ at } 291 \text{ K}$$

The *enthalpy of combustion* is the heat change when 1 mole of the substance is completely burnt in oxygen under stated conditions. The enthalpy of combustion of ethane is $-1559.8 \text{ kJ mol}^{-1}$ at 298 K:

$$C_2H_6 + 3\frac{1}{2}O_2 \rightarrow 2CO_2 + 3H_2O, \Delta H = -1559.8 \text{ kJ mol}^{-1}$$

Other values are given in Table 13.2. The heat of combustion is measured in a 'bomb calorimeter' (Fig. 13.3) which is filled with compressed oxygen and is air-tight. The substance is ignited electrically.

Table 13.2   Enthalpies of combustion at 298 K

Reaction	$\Delta H_{combustion}/\text{kJ mol}^{-1}$
$CO + \frac{1}{2}O_2 \rightarrow CO_2$	$- 283.0$
$CH_4 + 2O_2 \rightarrow CO_2 + 2H_2O(l)$	$- 890.4$
$C + O_2 \rightarrow CO_2$	$- 393.5$
$H_2 + \frac{1}{2}O_2 \rightarrow H_2O(l)$	$- 285.9$
$C_2H_5OH + 3O_2 \rightarrow 2CO_2 + 3H_2O(l)$	-1366.7

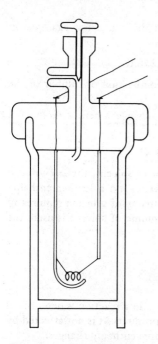

Fig. 13.3 A bomb calorimeter (the whole vessel is immersed in an insulated calorimeter containing water)

Table 13.3 Enthalpies of formation at 298 K

Substance	ΔH_f/kJ mol^{-1}
NH_3	$-$ 46.0
HCl	$-$ 92.3
HBr	$-$ 36.2
HI	$+$ 26.5
SO_3	$-$ 395.4
NO	$+$ 90.4
CH_4	$-$ 74.8
C_2H_6	$-$ 84.6
C_2H_4	$+$ 52.3
C_2H_2	$+$ 226.8
C_2H_5OH	$-$ 277.7

The *enthalpy of formation* is the enthalpy change when 1 mole of a substance is formed from its elements (in their most stable form) at the stated conditions.

$$\tfrac{1}{2}H_2(g) + \tfrac{1}{2}Cl_2(g) \rightarrow HCl(g), \quad \Delta H = -92.3 \text{ kJ mol}^{-1} \text{ at } 298 \text{ K}$$

For oxides the enthalpy of formation is equal to the enthalpy of combustion, provided 1 mole of the element gives 1 mole of the oxide. For example, in the reaction

$$S(s) + O_2(g) \rightarrow SO_2(g), \Delta H = -296.9 \text{ kJ mol}^{-1} \text{ at 298 K}$$

the enthalpy change is either the enthalpy of combustion of sulphur or the enthalpy of formation of sulphur dioxide.

The *enthalpy of solution* is the enthalpy change when 1 mole of a substance is dissolved in an excess of solvent.

$$HCl(g) + aq \rightarrow HCl(aq), \Delta H = -72 \text{ kJ mol}^{-1} \text{ (298 K)}$$

If the compound is dissolved in a small amount of solvent, the ΔH value is different from that using an excess of the solvent, and a further enthalpy change occurs on dilution. Theoretically, the enthalpy of solution requires an infinite amount of solvent, but when a large volume of solvent is used, the heat evolved on further dilution is negligible.

Hess' law

As illustrated in Fig. 13.1, the net energy change in a reaction is determined by the energy content of the reactants and the products. It is not affected by the intermediate stages. Figure 13.4 illustrates three enthalpy changes:

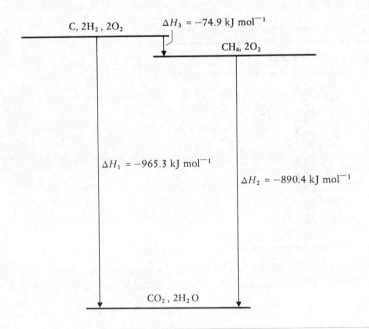

Fig. 13.4   Enthalpy changes in the formation and oxidation of methane

1. ΔH_1, the enthalpy of oxidation (by combustion) of carbon and hydrogen

   $C + 2H_2 + 2O_2 \rightarrow CO_2 + 2H_2O$;

2. ΔH_2, the enthalpy of combustion of methane to carbon dioxide and water

   $CH_4 + 2O_2 \rightarrow CO_2 + 2H_2O$;

3. ΔH_3, the enthalpy of formation of methane

   $C + 2H_2 \rightarrow CH_4$

Mathematically,

$\Delta H_1 = \Delta H_2 + \Delta H_3$

(It is essential to ensure that the arrows point in the same direction or else the sign must be changed.)

$\Delta H_3 = \Delta H_1 - \Delta H_2$

that is the enthalpy change for the direct formation of methane from its elements is equal to the net enthalpy change for its preparation *via* the carbon dioxide and water intermediates. This is stated in Hess's law: The enthalpy change in a chemical reaction is dependent only on the enthalpies of the initial reactants and final products and is independent of the intermediate path between the two.

It will also be seen from Fig. 13.4, that the enthalpy changes for the two reactions

$CH_4 + 2O_2 \rightarrow CO_2 + 2H_2O$

and

$CO_2 + 2H_2O \rightarrow CH_4 + 2O_2$

are equal in magnitude though opposite in sign, viz:

$CH_4 + 2O_2 \rightarrow CO_2 + 2H_2O, \Delta H_{298K}^{\ominus} = -890.4 \text{ kJ mol}^{-1}$
$CO_2 + 2H_2O \rightarrow CH_4 + 2O_2, \Delta H_{298K} = +890.4 \text{ kJ mol}^{-1}$

A useful application of the principle is in the determination of the enthalpies of formation. It is experimentally difficult to determine these values directly for many compounds. Some elements do not react, others react to give a mixture of products and so it is difficult to determine the ΔH_f values for the separate products. This can be illustrated for methane. The enthalpies of combusion are listed in Table 13.2. ΔH_1 is the sum of the enthalpies of combusion of 1 mole carbon and 2 moles hydrogen,

$\Delta H_1 = (-393.5) + 2(-285.9) = -965.3 \text{ kJ mol}^{-1}$
$\Delta H_2 = -890.4 \text{ kJ mol}^{-1}$

So,

$\Delta H_3 = \Delta H_1 - \Delta H_2$
$\Delta H_3 = (-965.3) - (-890.4)$
$\quad\ = -74.9$

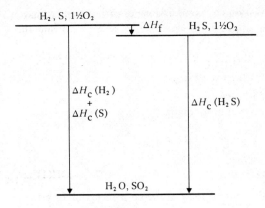

Fig. 13.5 Enthalpy changes for formation and combustion of hydrogen sulphide

So, $\Delta H_{f(298 \text{ K})}^{\circ}$ for methane is -74.9 kJ mol^{-1}.

The enthalpies of combustion of hydrogen (to liquid water), sulphur (to sulphur dioxide) and hydrogen sulphide are -285.9, -296.9 and -562.2 kJ mol^{-1} respectively. Calculate the enthalpy of formation of hydrogen sulphide.

Figure 13.5 illustrates the enthalpy changes for these reactions.

ΔH_f = enthalpy of combustion of reactants $-$ enthalpy of combustion of products

$= \Delta H_c(H_2) + \Delta H_c(S) - \Delta H_c(H_2S)$

$= (-285.9) + (-296.9) - (-562.2)$ kJ mol^{-1}

$= -20.6$ kJ mol^{-1}.

The same law of Hess can be applied to predict the enthalpy changes of reaction from the enthalpy changes of formation of the reacting species. Consider the reaction

$$CO(g) + H_2O(g) \rightarrow CO_2(g) + H_2(g)$$

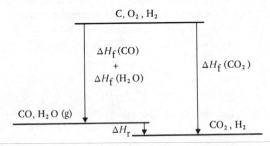

Fig. 13.6 Enthalpy changes of reaction of carbon monoxide and steam

Figure 13.6 illustrates the relationship between the enthalpies of formation of CO, $H_2O(g)$ and CO_2 and the enthalpy of reaction, ΔH_r. Substituting the values in Table 13.2:

$$\Delta H_r = \Delta H_f(CO_2) - [\Delta H_f(CO) + \Delta H_f(H_2O)]$$
$$= -393.5 - [(-110.5) + (-241.8)] \text{ kJ mol}^{-1}$$
$$= -393.5 + 110.5 + 241.8 \text{ kJ mol}^{-1}$$
$$= -41.2 \text{ kJ mol}^{-1}.$$

Calculate the enthalpy of reaction for

$$C_2H_4(g) + H_2O(g) \rightarrow C_2H_5OH(1)$$

given that the enthalpies of formation of C_2H_4, $H_2O(g)$ and $C_2H_5OH(1)$ are +52.3, −241.8 and −277.7 kJ mol^{-1} respectively.

Figure 13.7 illustrates the relationship.

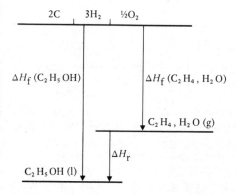

Fig. 13.7   Energy level diagram for the synthesis of ethanol

Enthalpy of reaction = enthalpy of formation of products − enthalpy of formation of reactants

$$\Delta H_r = \Delta H_f(C_2H_5OH) - \Delta H_f(C_2H_4) - \Delta H_f(H_2O)$$
$$= (-277.7) - (+52.3) - (-241.8) \text{ kJ mol}^{-1}$$
$$= -88.2 \text{ kJ mol}^{-1}$$

So, the enthalpy change on the production of ethanol from ethene and steam is −88.2 kJ mol^{-1}.

Summary

At the conclusion of this chapter, you should be able to:

1. give examples of several forms of energy;
2. give examples of systems that convert one energy form into another;
3. state what is meant by bond energy;

4. state the meaning of the symbols ΔU and ΔH;
5. state the conditons under which enthalpy changes are equal to heat changes;
6. distinguish between exothermic and endothermic reactions;
7. define the enthalpies of reaction, of neutralisation, of combustion, of formation and of solution;
8. describe methods for the determination of the enthalpies of reaction and combustion;
9. explain why a number of acids and bases give very similar enthalpies of neutralisation;
10. quote Hess's law;
11. determine the enthalpy of formation of a compound from the enthalpies of combustion of the elements and the compound;
12. calculate the enthalpy of reaction from the enthalpies of formation of the reactants and products.

Experiments

1. Determine the enthalpy of neutralisation of hydrochloric acid (*Selected Experiments in Physical Science;* D. H. Marrow (Longman, 1974), page 65).
2. Determine the enthalpy of solution and of hydration of copper sulphate (*Basic Chemistry for ONC;* O. B. Hayes, *et. al.* (A.S.E., 1973), expt. 1.1/5).
3. Determine the heat of reaction of zinc chloride and silver nitrate.
4. Determine the heat of formation of zinc iodide — place in a calorimeter 1.5 g iodine covered by 0.5 g zinc and a crystal of iodine; add a small squirt of water to catalyse the reaction.

References

Energy Changes in Chemistry; J. A. Allen (Blackie, 1975).

Filmloops

The Born—Haber cycle (Nuffield, Longman).
Energetics (Parts 1—3) (Longman).

Questions

1. State Hess's law and apply it to the determination of the enthalpy of formation of ethane, given that the enthalpies of combustion for carbon (to carbon dioxide), hydrogen (to water) and ethane are —394, —286 and —1561 kJ mol^{-1} respectively.

2. The enthalpies of combustion of hydrogen, carbon monoxide and methanol are -286, -283 and $-714\,kJ\,mol^{-1}$ respectively. What is the
   enthalpy change for the synthesis of methanol from carbon monoxide
   and water?

3. Aluminium metal reduces chromium(III) oxide to chromium and is
   converted to Al_2O_3. If the enthalpies of formation of Al_2O_3 and Cr_2O_3
   are -1596 and $-1134\,kJ\,mol^{-1}$ respectively, calculate the enthalpy
   change in the reduction reaction.

4. The enthalpies of combusion of sulphur, carbon and carbon disulphide
   are -297, -394 and $-1076\,kJ\,mol^{-1}$ respectively. Calculate the enthalpy of formation of carbon disulphide.

Chapter 14

Equilibrium

Some reactions, often by a variation of the controlling conditions, can be made to proceed either to the right or left of a chemical equation. For example, if bismuth(III) chloride is added to water, a white precipitate of bismuth oxochloride is formed:

$$BiCl_3 + H_2O \rightarrow BiOCl(s) + 2HCl(aq)$$

If, however, hydrochloric acid is added to bismuth oxochloride, a clear, colourless solution of bismuth(III) chloride is obtained. The above reaction has been reversed:

$$BiOCl(s) + 2HCl(aq) \rightarrow BiCl_3(aq) + H_2O$$

Many reactions give less than the expected yield of a product because the reaction has been partially reversed. For example, ethyl ethanoate (substance C) is prepared from ethanoic acid (A) and ethanol (B):

$$CH_3COOH + C_2H_5OH \rightarrow CH_3COOC_2H_5 + H_2O$$
$$\quad (A) \qquad\quad (B) \qquad\qquad (C)$$

But ethyl ethanoate is hydrolysed back to the acid and alcohol:

$$CH_3COOC_2H_5 + H_2O \leftarrow CH_3COOH + C_2H_5OH$$

So, as soon as the ethyl ethanoate is produced, some of it is hydrolysed back to the reactants. Eventually a balance is reached when ethyl ethanoate is hydrolysed as fast as it is produced. The composition of the mixture (A, B, C and water) does not vary; the system is said to be in *equilibrium*. This is indicated in the equation by the reversible arrows $\rightleftharpoons$:

$$CH_3COOH + C_2H_5OH \rightleftharpoons CH_3COOC_2H_5 + H_2O$$

In all equilibria, the rate of the forward reaction is equal to the rate of the reverse reaction. As a result, there is no change in the quantities of the components of the equilibria. Catalysts increase the speed of chemical reactions. In the case of systems that go to equilibrium, catalysts accelerate the forward and the reverse reactions equally. So, catalysts increase the rate at which equilibrium is attained and not the amounts of the components.

Equilibria are important states. Many industrial processes are in equilibrium (some are discussed at the end of the chapter) and many biological reactions are also in equilibrium. One important biological reaction is that between the molecule adenosine diphosphate (ADP for short) and inorganic phosphate (P_i). These react in the presence of magnesium ions in neutral solution to give adenosine triphosphate (ATP). The reaction is reversible and is an important source of biological energy:

$$ADP + P_i \rightleftharpoons ATP + H_2O, \quad \Delta H = -20 \text{ kJ mol}^{-1}$$

Energy is produced in biological cells through the oxidation of compounds such as glucose. The enthalpy change for the oxidation of glucose is -2850 kJ mol^{-1}. The cell is unable to cope with the release of so much energy in one lump, and so a controlled breakdown of glucose occurs. There are over twenty steps in this breakdown, each releasing small quantities of energy. The ADP–ATP equilibrium is involved in several of these steps.

Equilibrium constant

It is found that the ratio of the concentrations of products to reactants at equilibrium can be represented as a constant. For example, in the above reaction for the preparation of ethyl ethanoate:

$$K_c = \frac{[CH_3COOC_2H_5]_e \cdot [H_2O]_e}{[CH_3COOH]_e \cdot [C_2H_5OH]_e}$$

where K_c = equilibrium constant,
$[CH_3COOC_2H_5]_e$, etc. = equilibrium molar concentration of ester, etc.

In general, for a reaction of the general form

$$aA + bB \rightleftharpoons cC + dD$$

(A, B, C, D being the compounds in equilibrium; a, b, c, d indicating the number of moles present in the reaction),

$$K_c = \frac{[C]_e^c \cdot [D]_e^d}{[A]_e^a \cdot [B]_e^b}$$

174   K_c has a value which is typical of the reaction under consideration. It is dependent on the temperature of the reaction, but it is independent of catalysis (see above). The larger the value of K_c, the larger the proportion of products in the equilibrium mixture. For example, a value of 10 for K_c would indicate that the product term $[C]^c \cdot [D]^d$ is ten times larger than that for the reactants, $[A]^a \cdot [B]^b$. $K_c = 1\,000$ would imply that the product concentration term was one thousand times that for the reactants.

In the hydrolysis of bismuth(III) chloride, the relationship becomes

$$K_c = \frac{[BiOCl]_e \cdot [HCl]_e^2}{[BiCl_3]_e \cdot [H_2O]_e}$$

When 1 mole of each of ethanoic acid and ethanol are mixed and allowed to react to equilibrium, it is found that the amount of acid remaining is 0.33 moles. From the chemical equation

$$CH_3COOH + C_2H_5OH \rightleftharpoons CH_3COOC_2H_5 + H_2O$$

it is apparent that 1 mole of acid reacts with 1 mole of alcohol to give 1 mole of ester and 1 mole of water. The amount of acid consumed is $(1 - 0.33) = 0.67$ moles. So, 0.67 moles alcohol must also be consumed, leaving 0.33 moles, and 0.67 moles of both ester and water are produced. Since the volume is not specified, let it be considered to be V dm^3.

Equilibrium concentration of ethanoic acid = $0.33/V$ mol dm^{-3};
equilibrium concentration of ethanol = $0.33/V$ mol dm^{-3};
equilibrium concentration of ethyl ethanoate = $0.67/V$ mol dm^{-3};
equilibrium concentration of water = $0.67/V$ mol dm^{-3}.

So,

$$K_c = \frac{0.67/V \times 0.67/V}{0.33/V \times 0.33/V}$$
$$= 4$$

From a knowledge of the equilibrium constant it is possible to predict the yield of the reaction. For example, if a student uses 10 g of each reactant, what yield of ethyl ethanoate can he expect to get?

The initial number of moles of acid and alcohol are $\frac{10}{60}$ (=0.167) and $\frac{10}{46}$ (=0.217). If x moles of ester are produced, then x moles of acid and alcohol must have been consumed, and x moles of water are produced. So, the equilibrium concentrations are:

$[CH_3COOH]_e = (0.167 - x)/V$; $[C_2H_5OH]_e = (0.217 - x)/V$; $[CH_3COOC_2H_5]_e = x/V$; $[H_2O]_e = x/V$

$$K_c = 4 = \frac{x/V \cdot x/V}{(0.167 - x)/V \cdot (0.217 - x)/V}$$

So, $3x^2 - 1.536x + 0.145 = 0$

Hence, $x = 0.387$ or 0.125

(0.387 is an impossible answer — the student did not have that much acid to start with!) So, 0.125 moles of ester are produced, that is $0.125 \times 88 = 11$ g.

Gaseous systems

Many industrial processes involve gas phase reactions. For example, the preparation of sulphuric acid (via sulphur trioxide)

$$2SO_2 + O_2 \rightleftharpoons 2SO_3$$

the synthesis of ammonia

$$N_2 + 3H_2 \rightleftharpoons 2NH_3$$

and the oxidation of ammonia in the preparation of nitric acid

$$4NH_3 + 5O_2 \rightleftharpoons 4NO + 6H_2O$$

These systems can be treated in the same manner as the liquid systems already discussed. Consider the reaction between hydrogen and iodine vapour

$$H_2(g) + I_2(g) \rightleftharpoons 2HI(g)$$

We can write the equilibrium constant

$$K_c = \frac{[HI]_e^2}{[H_2]_e [I_2]_e}$$

and so calculate the value of K_c. However it is normally more convenient to measure quantities of gases by their pressures rather than concentrations. The pressure of a gas is proportional to its molar concentration:

$$P \cdot V = n \cdot R \cdot T \text{ (general gas equation)}$$

$$\therefore P = \frac{n}{V} \cdot R \cdot T = c \cdot R \cdot T$$

So, $P \alpha$ molar concentration (c) (at a constant temperature).
The equilibrium term can now be expressed as

$$K_p = \frac{P_{HI}^2}{P_{H_2} \cdot P_{I_2}}$$

where P_x is the equilibrium pressure of component X.
(N.B. K_c and K_p are not necessarily equal in value, though they are related.)
Since the pressure of a gas is related to the number of moles of that gas per unit of volume, the pressure of each component in a mixture is equal to the mole fraction multiplied by the total pressure. For example, if one-third of a gaseous mixture of total pressure 101.3 kPa is A, then the pressure of A is ($\frac{1}{3} \times 101.3$) kPa = 33.77 kPa.

In a reaction of equimolar quantities of hydrogen and iodine, it was found at equilibrium that there were 0.11 moles of hydrogen, 0.11 moles of iodine and 0.78 moles hydrogen iodide. The total pressure at equilibrium was 597.7 kPa. What is the value of K_p?
Total number of moles = (2 × 0.11) + 0.78 = 1.00 moles.
Fraction of hydrogen in the mixture = $\frac{0.11}{1.00}$ = 0.11;
so, pressure of hydrogen = 0.11 × 597.7 = 65.75 kPa.
Similarly, pressure of iodine = 65.75 kPa.

The pressure of hydrogen iodide = 0.78 × 597.7 = 466.21 kPa.
So,

$$K_p = \frac{P_{HI}^2}{P_{H_2} \cdot P_{I_2}} = \frac{466.21^2}{65.75 \times 65.75}$$

$$= 50.28$$

As with liquids, we can use the equilibrium constant to predict yields. For example, nitrogen and oxygen react to give nitrogen(II) oxide at high temperatures. If $K_p = 2.9 \times 10^{-2}$ at 2000°C for the reaction

$$\tfrac{1}{2}N_2(g) + \tfrac{1}{2}O_2(g) \rightleftharpoons NO(g)$$

what is the percentage of nitrogen(II) oxide formed when air (79 per cent nitrogen, 21 per cent oxygen by volume) is heated to this temperature?

For gases, the number of moles is proportional to the volume. So, air contains 0.79 moles nitrogen to 0.21 moles oxygen. So, if the amount of nitrogen converted is x, then

the amount of nitrogen at equilibrium is $(0.79 - x)$,
the amount of oxygen at equilibrium is $(0.21 - x)$,

(since they react in equal proportions according to the equation), and the fraction of nitrogen(II) oxide is $2x$. Therefore, the equilibrium pressures are:

$$P_{N_2} = \frac{(0.79 - x)}{1.00} \times 101.3$$

$$P_{O_2} = \frac{(0.21 - x)}{1.00} \times 101.3$$

and

$$P_{NO} = \frac{2x}{1.00} \times 101.3$$

(The total number of moles at equilibrium is $(0.79 - x) + (0.21 - x) + 2x = 1.00$, and the total pressue is 101.3 kPa).
For the equilibrium,

$$K_p = \frac{P_{NO}}{P_{N_2}^{1/2} \cdot P_{O_2}^{1/2}}$$

$$= 2.9 \times 10^{-2}$$

So,

$$2.9 \times 10^{-2} = \frac{2x \cdot 101.3}{[(0.79 - x) \cdot 101.3]^{1/2}[(0.21 - x) \cdot 101.3]^{1/2}}$$

Hence,

$$x = 5.8 \times 10^{-3}$$

The fraction of nitrogen(II) oxide is, therefore, $\dfrac{(5.8 \times 10^{-3} \times 2)}{1.00}$

that is, *1.16* per cent.

Ionic product

Water is a covalent molecule but it is slightly ionised:

$$H_2O \rightleftharpoons H^+(aq) + OH^-(aq)$$

$$K_c = \frac{[H^+]_e [OH^-]_e}{[H_2O]_e}$$

The concentration of the ions is very small (10^{-7} mol dm^{-3} at 298 K). In contrast, the concentration of undissociated water molecules is very large. Even for large changes in the ionic concentrations, the relative changes in $[H_2O]$ are very small, so it can be considered to be constant:

$$K_w = K_c \cdot [H_2O]_e = [H^+]_e [OH^-]_e$$
$$= 10^{-7} \cdot 10^{-7}$$
$$= 10^{-14}$$

K_w is a constant for water if the temperature is constant. It is known as the *ionic product for water*. The value of K_w is temperature dependent.

The ionic product can be deduced from a study of the conductivity of water. Pure water has a specific conductivity of

$$\kappa = 0.055 \times 10^{-4} \text{ ohm}^{-1} \text{ m}^{-1}.$$

$$\Lambda = \frac{10^{-3} \cdot \kappa}{M}$$

The molarity is 55.51 M (i.e. there are 55.51 moles H_2O per dm^3 of water), so

$$\Lambda = \frac{10^{-3} \times 0.055 \times 10^{-4}}{55.51}$$
$$= 9.73 \times 10^{-11} \text{ ohm}^{-1} \text{ m}^2 \text{ mol}^{-1}$$

If the water were completely ionised, the molar conductivity (i.e. Λ_0) would be $(349.6 + 199.1) \times 10^{-4} = 548.7 \times 10^{-4} \text{ ohm}^{-1} \text{ m}^2 \text{ mol}^{-1}$ (Table 12.2).

$$\text{Degree of dissociation} = \frac{100 \cdot \Lambda}{\Lambda_0}$$
$$= \frac{100 \times 9.73 \times 10^{-11}}{548.7 \times 10^{-4}}$$
$$= 1.81 \times 10^{-7} \text{ per cent}$$

As $[H_2O] = 55.51\,M$,

the number of moles of dissociated water molecules per dm^3

$$= \frac{1.81 \times 10^{-7}}{100} \times 55.51$$
$$= 1.00 \times 10^{-7}$$

Since 1 mole of dissociated H_2O produces 1 mole $H^+(aq)$,

$$[H^+] = 1.00 \times 10^{-7} M$$

Since $[OH^-] = [H^+] = 10^{-7} M$,

$$K_w = 10^{-7} \cdot 10^{-7}$$
$$= 10^{-14}$$

Ionisation of Acids

Acids react with water to produce hydroxonium ions

$$HA + H_2O \rightleftharpoons H_3O^+ + A^-$$

So, the equilibrium constant is

$$K_c = \frac{[H_3O^+]_e [A^-]_e}{[HA]_e [H_2O]_e}$$

$[H_2O]_e$ is constant for a dilute solution, so

$$K_a = \frac{[H_3O^+]_e [A^-]_e}{[HA]_e}$$

where K_a is the *dissociation constant* of the acid (also known as the *ionisation constant*).

Consider an M molar ethanoic acid solution, $K_a = 2 \times 10^{-5}$. If the degree of dissociation is α (i.e. a fraction α dissociates), then of M moles HA (where $A = CH_3COO$), $(M - M\alpha)$ moles remain at equilibrium. Since 1 mole HA dissociates into 1 mole H^+ and 1 mole A^-, $M\alpha$ moles of HA generate $M\alpha$ moles H^+, $M\alpha$ moles A^-.

$$K_a = \frac{[H_3O^+] [CH_3COO^-]}{[CH_3COOH]}$$

$$2 \times 10^{-5} = \frac{M\alpha \cdot M\alpha}{M(1 - \alpha)}$$

$$= \frac{M\alpha^2}{(1 - \alpha)}$$

When $M = 0.1$,
$\alpha = 0.014$
So, $[H_3O^+] = 0.1 \times 0.014$
$= 1.4 \times 10^{-3}$

pH scale

The strength of an acid is determined by its degree of dissociation. The strong acids have high values of $[H^+(aq)]$ (or $[H_3O^+]$); weak acids, such as ethanoic acid, have relatively low values. A convenient scale of acid strength is the pH scale, where

$$pH = -\log_{10}[H^+(aq)]$$

So, for the above reaction

$$pH = -\log_{10}(1.4 \times 10^{-3})$$
$$= 2.85$$

In water, a neutral solution, $[H^+] = 10^{-7}M$, so $pH = -\log 10^{-7} = 7$. Hydrochloric acid is completely dissociated in solution

$$HCl(aq) \rightarrow H^+(aq) + Cl^-(aq)$$

179

so a $0.1\,M$ solution contains 0.1 mol dm^{-3} of hydrogen ion,

and pH $= -\log_{10}0.1 = 1$

Table 14.1 gives a series of values of K_a, M, $[H^+]$, α and pH for a selection of weak acids.

Table 14.1 Hydrogen ion concentration of weak acids

Acid	Dissociation constant	Molarity	$[H^+]$	Percentage dissociation	pH
CH$_3$COOH	1.80×10^{-5}	0.20	1.91×10^{-3}	0.95	2.72
		0.10	1.35×10^{-3}	1.34	2.87
		0.05	9.58×10^{-4}	1.90	3.02
		0.01	4.33×10^{-4}	4.24	3.36
C$_6$H$_5$COOH	6.00×10^{-5}	0.20	3.49×10^{-3}	1.73	2.46
		0.10	2.48×10^{-3}	2.45	2.61
		0.05	1.76×10^{-3}	3.46	2.75
		0.01	8.05×10^{-4}	7.75	3.09
H$_3$BO$_3$	5.55×10^{-10}	0.20	1.05×10^{-5}	0.005	4.98
		0.10	7.45×10^{-6}	0.007	5.13
		0.05	5.27×10^{-6}	0.010	5.28
		0.01	2.36×10^{-6}	0.024	5.63
HF	5.62×10^{-4}	0.20	1.09×10^{-2}	5.30	1.96
		0.10	7.78×10^{-3}	7.50	2.11
		0.05	2.67×10^{-3}	10.60	2.25
		0.01	1.06×10^{-5}	23.71	2.57

Ostwald's law

Consider a weak acid, HA, in dilute solution (M molar) and with a degree of dissociation α.

$$HA(aq) + H_2O \rightleftharpoons H_3O^+(aq) + A^-(aq)$$

$$K_a = \frac{[H_3O^+]_e[A^-]_e}{[HA]_e}$$

We have an M molar solution of HA of which $M\alpha$ moles have dissociated into $M\alpha$ moles of each of H_3O^+ and A^- per dm^3 of solution. So,

$$K_a = \frac{(M\alpha) \cdot (M\alpha)}{(M - M\alpha)}$$

$$= \frac{M\alpha^2}{(1 - \alpha)}$$

If the acid is weak $(1 - \alpha) \approx 1$, (e.g. for $0.20\,M$ ethanoic acid, $(1 - \alpha) = (1 - 0.009\,5) \approx 1$).

Therefore, $K_a \approx M \cdot \alpha^2$

This is stated in Ostwald's law which says that, for a *dilute* solution of a *weak* electrolyte, the degree of dissociation is inversely proportional to the square root of the molarity, i.e. it is proportional to $\sqrt{1/M}$. The difference between the approximate figures and the exact values is usually negligible. For example, for $0.2\,M$ ethanoic acid $\alpha = 0.95$ per cent (exact method) or 0.94 per cent (approximation). In both cases the pH is 2.72.

Bases

Bases can be integrated into the pH scale. Consider $0.1\,M$ sodium hydroxide solution.

$$NaOH(aq) \rightarrow Na^+(aq) + OH^-(aq)$$

This is a strong electrolyte, so the hydroxide ion concentration, $[OH^-]$, is 0.1. But, in aqueous solution at 298 K the relationship

$$K_w = [H^+][OH^-] = 10^{-14}$$

must hold. So

$$[H^+] = 10^{-14}/0.1$$
$$= 10^{-13}$$
and pH $= -\log_{10}[H^+]$
$$= 13$$

Figure 14.1 shows diagrammatically the general relationship between pH and the acidity/bascity of a solution. It is possible to have pH values outside the range 0–14, but most common dilute solutions can be considered to be within the range. (For concentrated solutions, some of the relationships described above do not hold exactly.)

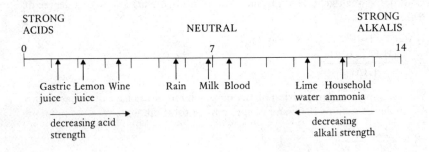

Fig. 14.1 The pH scale

For weak bases we can write an equilibrium expression as for acids.

$$NH_3(aq) + H_2O \rightleftharpoons NH_4^+(aq) + OH^-(aq)$$

$$K_b = \frac{[NH_4^+][OH^-]}{[NH_3]}$$

For ammonia solution, $NH_3(aq)$, the K_b value is 1.74×10^{-5}.

It is useful to employ the terms pK_a and pK_b which have a meaning similar to pH:

$$pH = -\log_{10}[H^+]$$
$$pK_a = -\log_{10} K_a$$
$$pK_b = -\log_{10} K_b$$

So, pK_a for ethanoic acid is $-\log_{10}(1.80 \times 10^{-5}) = 4.74$;
pK_b for ammonia solution is $-\log_{10}(1.74 \times 10^{-5}) = 4.76$.
It can be shown that pK_a and pK_b are related through the ionic product for water (as applied in the use of the pH scale) and so,

$$pK_a = 14.0 - pK_b$$

So, for ammonia solution,

$$pK_a = 14.0 - 4.76 = 9.24$$

Salts

Many salts are partially hydrolysed by water to produce solutions which are either acidic or basic. For example, sodium hydrogen carbonate solution is basic due to the production of hydroxide ions:

$$Na^+(aq) + HCO_3^-(aq) + H_2O \rightleftharpoons Na^+(aq) + H_2CO_3 + OH^-(aq)$$

The salt is prepared from a weak acid (H_2CO_3) and a strong base (NaOH), and so is described as the salt of a weak acid and a strong base. Such salts are always basic. Similarly, sodium ethanoate is basic:

$$Na^+(aq) + CH_3COO^-(aq) + H_2O \rightleftharpoons Na^+ + CH_3COOH + OH^-(aq)$$

Ammonium chloride is prepared from a strong acid (HCl aq) and a weak base (NH_3 aq) and is acidic in solution:

$$NH_4^+(aq) + Cl^-(aq) + H_2O \rightleftharpoons NH_3(aq) + H^+(aq) + Cl^-(aq)$$

These solutions can be tested for acidic or basic character by the use of a pH meter.

Sodium chloride, a salt of both a strong acid and a strong base, is neutral:

$$Na^+(aq) + Cl^-(aq) + H_2O \rightarrow Na^+(aq) + Cl^-(aq) + H_2O$$

Weak acid—weak base salts may be either acidic or basic depending on the relative strengths of the acid and base.

Water has a pH of 7. What is the pH of a solution prepared from 1 cm^3 1 M hydrochloric acid added to 1 dm^3 of water? The amount of acid added is 10^{-3} mole, so the concentration of the acidified solution is 10^{-3} mol dm^{-3}. Since the acid is a strong electrolyte, its pH $= -\log_{10}10^{-3} = 3$. So, the addition of 1 cm^3 of 1 M acid to 1 dm^3 of water causes its pH to drop from 7 to 3. In the body, the blood is of pH 7.4. If the pH goes outside the range 7.2–7.6, the result is fatal.

The pH is controlled by means of buffer solutions; these are, for example, solutions of salts of weak acids and their salts. A *buffer solution* is a solution whose pH is fairly constant even on the addition of small amounts of acid and alkali.

One buffer solution is prepared from sodium ethanoate in ethanoic acid solution. The sodium ethanoate dissociates into its constituents ions, and the ethanoic acid is partially dissociated into ions:

$CH_3COONa(aq) \rightarrow CH_3COO^-(aq) + Na^+(aq)$
$CH_3COOH(aq) \rightleftharpoons CH_3COO^-(aq) + H^+(aq)$

If acid is added, that is hydrogen ions, these combine with the ethanoate ions to produce more ethanoic acid molecules since this is a weak acid.

$CH_3COO^-(aq) + H^+(aq) \rightarrow CH_3COOH(aq)$

If hydroxide ions are added, these combine with hydrogen ions of ethanoic acid; more acid molecules dissociate to replace the reacted hydrogen ions.

$H^+(aq) + OH^-(aq) \rightleftharpoons H_2O$

Consider a mixture of 0.350 mole ethanoic acid and 0.650 mole sodium ethanoate in 1 dm^3 of solution.

$$K_a = \frac{[H^+][CH_3COO^-]}{[CH_3COOH]} = 1.85 \times 10^{-5}$$

The ethanoate ion concentration is due to the sodium ethanoate (0.650 mole) and a small amount from the ethanoic acid. This latter amount is negligible compared to that from the sodium salt. So, $[CH_3COO^-] \approx 0.650\,M$. The ethanoic acid concentration is 0.350 M less a small amount due to the dissociation of the acid, so $[CH_3COOH] \approx 0.350\,M$.

$$1.85 \times 10^{-5} = [H^+] \times \frac{0.650}{0.350}$$

$$[H^+] = 1.85 \times 10^{-5} \times \frac{0.350}{0.650}$$

$$= 9.96 \times 10^{-6}$$

$$\therefore pH = 5.00$$

We now add 1 cm^3 1 M hydrochloric acid, that is 10^{-3} moles. This combines with ethanoate ions to form ethanoic acid molecules. So the concentration of ethanoate ions is $(0.650-0.001) = 0.649\,M$. The concentration of ethanoic acid molecules is increased by the same amount; $(0.350 + 0.001) = 0.351\,M$ which is the new concentration of the undissociated acid.

So,

$$1.85 \times 10^{-5} = [H^+] \times \frac{0.649}{0.351}$$

$$[H^+] = 1.85 \times 10^{-5} \times \frac{0.351}{0.649}$$

$$= 1.00 \times 10^{-5}$$

$$pH = 5.00$$

The ethanoate solution has effectively buffered the solution at pH 5. In, fact, it is possible to add up to 5 cm^3 1 M hydrochloric acid without any change in the pH value 5.00. The addition of 10 cm^3 of this acid has only a small effect (pH 4.98).

Each buffer solution has a characteristic known as its *buffer capacity*. This is the amount of acid or alkali that can be added to the solution without it suffering a change in pH. It is found that buffer solutions are not satisfactory if the pH of the solution lies outside the range

$$pH = pK_a \pm 1$$

These ranges are given in Table 14.2 for some buffer mixtures. The exact pH of the solution is determined by the proportions of salt and acid.

Table 14.2 Buffer solutions

pH range	Buffer mixture
3–6	$CH_3COOH-CH_3COONa$
6–8	$NaH_2PO_4-Na_2HPO_4$
8–11	$Na_2B_4O_7-NaOH$
11	NH_4Cl-NH_3

The blood-stream is buffered at pH 7.4 by means of carbon dioxide and hydrogen carbonate ions (HCO_3^-). The pK_a value for dissolved carbon dioxide in the blood is 6.1.

$$CO_2 + H_2O \rightleftharpoons H_2CO_3 \rightleftharpoons H^+(aq) + HCO_3^-(aq)$$

$$K_a = \frac{[H^+][HCO_3^-]}{[H_2CO_3]}$$

If the pH = 7.4, then $[H^+] = 4.0 \times 10^{-8}$, so

$$\frac{[HCO_3^-]}{[H_2CO_3]} = \frac{8.0 \times 10^{-7}}{4.0 \times 10^{-8}} = \frac{20}{1}$$

So, to maintain a pH of 7.4, the ratio of the concentrations of HCO_3^- to H_2CO_3 must be 20:1.

Indicators

In Chapter 12 we noted that the pH of a solution could be determined by the use of a pH meter. An alternative method is to use compounds called 'indicators'. These are compounds that exist in two forms — one in an acidic medium, another in basic conditions. For example, phenolphthalein has two forms:

Colourless form   Pink form

Similarly, methyl orange has a red 'acid form' and a yellow anion ('basic form'). The K_a value for the indicators is, of course, different as for any other acid. Consequently, the hydrogen ion concentration or pH at which the individual indicators change colour is characteristic of the indicator. In practice the colour changes from one colour to another over a range of pH values called the *working range* (Table 14.3).

Table 14.3   Working ranges of some indicators

Working range	Indicator	'Acid form'	'Basic form'
1.2—2.8	thymol blue	red	yellow
3.1—4.4	methyl orange	orange	yellow
4.2—6.3	methyl red	red	yellow
6.0—8.0	litmus	red	blue
8.0—9.6	thymol blue	yellow	blue
8.3—10.0	phenolphthalein	colourless	pink

Thymol blue occurs twice in Table 14.3 because it has two structural changes each of which is accompanied by a colour change. By careful choice of indicators it is possible to determine the approximate pH of a solution. For example, if a solution turns litmus red, it must have a pH below 7. If the same solution turns methyl red yellow, then the pH must be above 5.3. So, the solution has a pH between 5.3 and 7.0.

It is possible to prepare a mixture of indicators so that there is a gradual colour change over a range of pH values. Such an indicator is called a *Universal indicator.*

Titrations

Consider a titration between a strong acid and a strong base. We will add $0.100\,M$ sodium hydroxide solution to $25.00\,cm^3$ $0.100\,M$ hydrochloric acid. Initially, the pH of the solution is 1.0. After the addition of 20 cm³ of the alkali, 5 cm³ of the acid remain unneutralised: 5 cm³ of $0.100\,M$ acid contain 5×10^{-4} moles HCl. The total volume of solution is $(25 + 20)$ cm³, so

$$[H^+] = 5 \times 10^{-4} \times \frac{1000}{45}\ M.$$ The pH is, therefore, 1.95.

Similarly, after 24 cm³ alkali have been added,
$[H^+] = 2.04 \times 10^{-3}$, pH = 2.69;
after 24.5 cm³ alkali, $[H^+] = 1.01 \times 10^{-3}$, pH = 3.00;
after 24.9 cm³ alkali, $[H^+] = 2.00 \times 10^{-4}$, pH = 3.70.
After the addition of 25.1 cm³ alkali, $[OH^-] = 2.00 \times 10^{-3}$,
so $[H^+] = 10^{-14}/2.00 \times 10^{-3} = 5.00 \times 10^{-12}$, pH = 11.30;
after 26.0 cm³ alkali, $[OH^-] = 1.96 \times 10^{-2}$, $[H^+] = 5.10 \times 10^{-13}$,
pH = 12.29;
after the addition of 50 cm³ alkali, $[OH^-] = 3.33 \times 10^{-2}$, $[H^+] = 3.00 \times 10^{-13}$,
pH = 12.52.

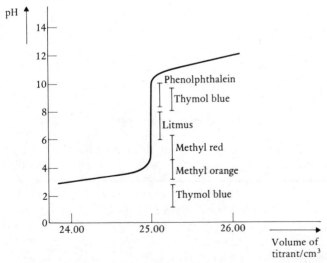

Fig. 14.2 Titration curve for 25.00 cm³ $0.100\,M$ strong acid with $0.100\,M$ strong alkali

These results are plotted in Fig. 14.2. It can be observed that there is a large change in pH at the end-point. Superimposed on the graph are the working ranges of some indicators. It can be seen that within 0.1 cm³ at the end-point all the indicators listed, except methyl orange, change colour. In practice even the methyl orange is sensitive enough to detect the end-point accurately.

Similar calculations can be used for weak acids or bases titrated with a strong reagent. In this case the K_a or K_b values must be taken into account. The titration curves are shown in Fig. 14.3. Which indicators are the most suitable for these titrations (i.e. completely change colour within 0.1 cm³ of the end-point)?

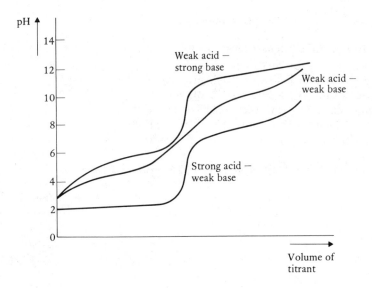

Fig. 14.3   Further titration curves

A comparison of the strong acid-weak base curve with Table 14.3 indicates that methyl orange and methyl red would be suitable indicators. Thymol blue and phenolphthalein would be suitable indicators for the weak acid—strong base titrations. With weak acid—weak base titrations, the pH changes very slowly at the end-point and is too insensitive for analysis. For example, it would need 2 cm³ of titrant to change the colour of litmus.

Some titrations have two sharp changes in pH. For example, when sodium carbonate is titrated with hydrochloric acid, two reactions occur successively (Fig. 14.4):

$$Na_2CO_3 + HCl \rightarrow NaHCO_3 + NaCl \text{ (phenolphthalein)}$$
$$NaHCO_3 + HCl \rightarrow NaCl + H_2O + CO_2 \text{ (methyl orange)}$$

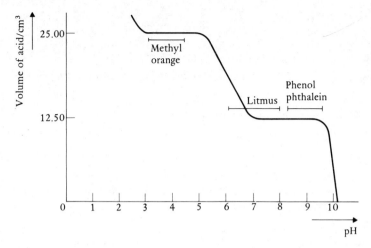

Fig. 14.4 The titration of 25.00 cm^3 $0.100\,M$ NA_2CO_3 (aq) with $0.100\,M$ hydrochloric acid

In a similar way, phosphoric acid has three successive reactions:

$H_3PO_4 + NaOH \rightarrow NaH_2PO_4 + H_2O$ (methyl orange)
$NaH_2PO_4 + NaOH \rightarrow Na_2HPO_4 + H_2O$ (phenolphthalein)
$Na_2HPO_4 + NaOH \rightarrow Na_3PO_4 + H_2O$ (no satisfactory indicator)

Le Chatelier's principle

When a reaction has reached equilibrium, the yield of the products can be affected further by certain changes. The principle which controls this was given by Le Chatelier: If a change is made in a factor affecting a system in equilibrium, then the system will move so as to minimise that change. Three factors have to be considered, concentration of the participating chemicals, pressure and temperature.

(a) Concentration

Prepare four mixtures of 25 cm^3 each of $0.1\,M$ solutions of iron(III) chloride and ammonium thiocyanate. The first mixture is used as a standard. To the second add 5 cm^3 concentrated iron(III) chloride solution. To another mixture add 5 cm^3 concentrated ammonium thiocyanate solution. To the final mixture add 10 cm^3 ammonium chloride solution. What do you observe in each case? The reaction is

$FeCl_3(aq) + 3NH_4CNS(aq) \rightleftharpoons Fe(CNS)_3(aq) + 3NH_4Cl(aq)$

The red colour is due to the iron(III) thiocyanate. If iron(III) chloride is added to the equilibrium mixture, then, according to Le Chatelier's principle, the system will adjust so as to reduce the concentration of the iron(III)

chloride, that is it will move to the right of the equation. The result is an increase in the concentration of the products and so a deepening of the colour. Similarly, the addition of ammonium thiocyanate causes the reaction to move to the right, and again an increase in the intensity of the colour.

Ammonium chloride solution is added in the last case. According to Le Chatelier's principle, the system must adjust to counter this change; it must move to the left to reduce the amount of ammonium chloride. This also reduces the concentration of the iron(III) thiocyanate and so the colour becomes less intense.

(b) Pressure

Pressure has a negligible effect on systems which do not involve gases. The pressure of a gas at constant volume and temperature is proportional to the number of moles of gas.

$$P \cdot V = n \cdot R \cdot T$$
$$\therefore P \propto n$$

Phosphorus(V) chloride decomposes in the gaseous phase to phosphorus(III) chloride and chlorine:

$$PCl_5(g) \rightleftharpoons PCl_3(g) + Cl_2(g)$$

If the pressure is increased, the system must move so as to reduce the pressure. This can be done by reducing the number of moles. The left hand side of the equation represents 1 mole of chemicals; the right hand side has two moles (one each of PCl_3 and Cl_2). So, the pressure is reduced by a movement to the left ($2 \rightarrow 1$ moles), that is the decomposition is suppressed.

(c) Temperature

An increase in temperature arises from an increase in heat supplied. The system must, therefore, adjust to absorb the extra heat. Dinitrogen tetroxide is a pale gas (yellow) in equilibrium with the much darker, brown nitrogen dioxide:

$$N_2O_4 \rightleftharpoons 2NO_2, \quad \Delta H = +62 \text{ kJ mol}^{-1}$$

The reaction is endothermic so the reaction absorbs heat when it moves to the right. If this system is heated, it will increase the proportion of nitrogen dioxide; it will deepen in colour.

Industrial applications

(a) Ammonia production

$$N_2 + 3H_2 \rightleftharpoons 2NH_3, \quad \Delta H = -92 \text{ kJ mol}^{-1}$$

An application of Le Chatelier's principle shows that a high pressure and a low temperature favour the production of ammonia. High pressure would cause the reaction to move to the right ($4 \rightarrow 2$ moles); the reaction moves to

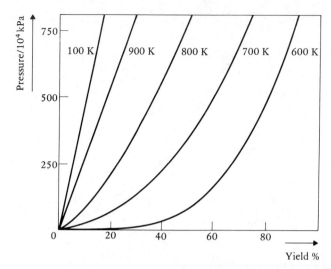

Fig. 14.5 Physical effects on the yield of ammonia

the left to absorb heat (a decrease in yield). While a high pressure is suitable (2.5×10^4 kPa is a normal situation, though higher pressure up to 10^5 kPa are also used), a low temperature is not practicable as this would make the reaction too slow. Industrially, a high yield is no use if the firm has to wait several years to get it! Fortunately it is possible to use a moderate temperature (800 K) and a catalyst (iron oxide with alkaline oxides) to accelerate the reaction. Figure. 14.5 illustrates the variation in yield with pressure and temperature. At 2.5×10^4 kPa and 800 K the yield obtained industrially is 15 per cent; the unchanged gases are recycled for further reaction.

(b) Sulphuric acid manufacture

The key step in the manufacture of the acid is the preparation of sulphur trioxide:

$$2SO_2 + O_2 \rightleftharpoons 2SO_3, \quad \Delta H = -189 \text{ kJ mol}^{-1}$$

Application of Le Chatelier's principle implies that the best conditions are, as for ammonia, low temperature and high pressure. In practice, K_p is so large at the lower temperatures ($K_p = 4\ 180$ at 600 K) that pressure has very little effect and it is uneconomic to use pressures above 150–200 kPa. As for ammonia production, a compromise temperature has to be used with a catalyst: 700 K with alkaline vanadium(V) oxide catalyst. As Fig. 14.6 shows, even at this temperature the conversion is very high and the overall yield is over 95 per cent.

(c) Nitrogen(II) oxide production

Another important acid is nitric acid. A possible route to this is the conversion of air to the gas nitrogen(II) oxide:

$$N_2 + O_2 \rightleftharpoons 2NO, \quad \Delta H = +180.6 \text{ kJ mol}^{-1}$$

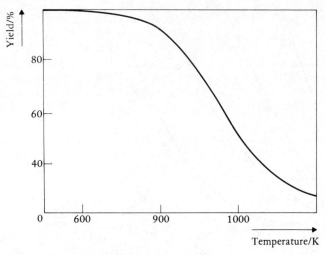

Fig. 14.6 Variation in the yield of SO_3

(Most nitrogen(II) oxide is produced by the oxidation of ammonia.) In this case pressure has no effect — there is no change in the number of moles on moving from left to right. But the reaction is endothermic, so the supply of heat favours the production of the oxide; the formation of the oxide absorbs the heat in accordance with Le Chatelier's principle. The yields are low, even at high temperatures (see Table 14.4), hence the fact that this is not extensively used industrially.

Table 14.4 Yield of nitrogen(II) oxide from air

Temperature/K	Yield/%
1500	0.1
2000	1
3000	4

(d) Hydrogen production

Hydrogen is obtained by reaction between carbon monoxide and steam:

$$CO(g) + H_2O(g) \rightleftharpoons CO_2(g) + H_2(g), \quad \Delta H = +41 \text{ kJ mol}^{-1}$$

There is no change in the number of moles of gas as the reaction proceeds, so pressure has no effect. Since the reaction is endothermic, an increase in the heat supply causes an increase in the yield of hydrogen. An excess of steam also shifts the reaction to the right, favouring the production of hydrogen. In practice, the most economical conditions are normal atmospheric pressure, excess steam, a temperature of 800 K and the use of a catalyst (mixed iron and chromium oxides).

$$C_2H_4(g) + H_2O(g) \rightleftharpoons C_2H_5OH(g), \quad \Delta H = -44 \text{ kJ mol}^{-1}$$

The practical conditions used are high pressure (6.8×10^3 kPa), moderate temperature (600 K) and a catalyst (phosphoric acid absorbed on 'Celite'). The yield of ethanol is optimum at this temperature taking into account both equilibrium and kinetic effects.

Summary

At the conclusion of this chapter, you should be able to:

1. state the meaning of equilibrium;
2. state that at equilibrium the rates of the forward and reverse reactions are equal;
3. write the expression for the equilibrium constant of a reaction in terms of the molar concentrations or partial pressures of the species in equilibrium;
4. calculate the equilibrium concentrations (or pressures) of the components in equilibrium and hence the equilibrium constant;
5. define the ionic product for water;
6. define the dissociation constant for an acid;
7. determine the relationship between the molarity, degree of dissociation and dissociation constant of an acid;
8. explain what is meant by the pH scale;
9. calculate the pH of a weak acid from its dissociation constant and concentration;
10. state Ostwald's law;
11. relate the terms pK_a and pK_b to the dissociation constants of acids and bases respectively;
12. explain why many salts have pH values other than 7;
13. explain what is meant by a buffer solution;
14. explain the action of a buffer solution;
15. calculate the pH of a buffer solution;
16. state what is meant by the buffer capacity;
17. define an indicator;
18. explain the action of an indicator;
19. define the working range of a given selection of indicators;
20. calculate the pH changes during an acid--base titration;
21. predict the most suitable indicator for a titration from its titration curve;
22. state Le Chatelier's principle;
23. apply Le Chatelier's principle in order to understand qualitatively the conditions used in industrial processes.

Experiments

1. Determine the equilibrium constant for the hydrolysis of ethyl ethanoate by titration.
2. Determine the equilibrium constant of electrochemical reactions (*Nuffield Advanced Science, Chemistry* Longman, 1970, expt. 17.3b).
3. Examine the stability of a buffer solution (*Basic Chemistry for ONC;* O. B. Hayes *et al.* (A.S.E., 1973, expt. 5.4(ii)).
4. Determine the working range of an indicator using a range of solutions of known pH.
5. Titrations (*Selected Experiments in Physical Science; D. H. Marrow* (Longman, 1974), Ch. 6).

References

Acid–base chemistry in the human body; *Nuffield Advanced Science, Chemistry, Student Book II* (Longman, 1970), 104–12.
Le Chatelier, common sense and metaphysics; A. Standen, *J. Chem. Educ.,* 1958, **35**, 132.
Le Chatelier, scientific principle or 'sacred cow'?; J. de Heer, *J. Chem. Educ.,* 1958, **35**, 133.
Principles of Titrimetric Analysis; E. E. Aynsley and A. B. Littlewood, R.I.C. Teachers Monograph No. 6 (Royal Institute of Chemistry, 1962).
Physical chemistry of ammonia synthesis; J. H. J. Peet, *Sch. Sci. Rev.,* 1974, **56**, 112–14.
Physical chemistry of sulphuric acid manufacture; J. H. J. Peet, *Sch. Sci. Rev.,* 1972, **53**, 762–5.

Films

Ammonia (I.C.I.).
Nitric acid (CHEM Study).
Equilibrium (CHEM Study).
Acid–base indicators (CHEM Study).
Titration of a weak acid (*Encyclopaedia Britannica*).

Questions

1. State Le Chatelier's principle. How is a reaction yield affected by temperature? From the data given in the table (page 193), determine the equilibrium constant for the formation of ethyl ethanoate at each temperature, and deduce whether the reaction is exothermic or endothermic.
2. Calculate the equilibrium constant for the formation of ammonia from 1 part nitrogen and 3 parts hydrogen by volume at a pressure of 250 kPa

Temperature/K	Equilibrium concentrations/mol dm^{-3}			
	Ethanoic acid	Ethanol	Ethyl ethanoate	Water
293	0.25	0.39	0.21	1.85
313	0.48	0.16	0.38	0.81
333	0.32	0.27	0.43	0.81

and a temperature of 700 K, if 40 per cent of the equilibrium mixture is ammonia.

3. The dissociation constant of benzoic acid is 6.6×10^{-5} at 298 K. If the concentration of the solution is $0.006\,M$, what is the degree of dissociation?

4. What is a buffer solution? What would be the pH of a solution containing equimolar quantities of ethanoic acid and sodium ethanoate? (K_a for ethanoic acid $= 1.9 \times 10^{-5}$ at 293 K).

5. What volume of $0.1\,M$ sodium methanoate must be added to 1 dm^3 of $0.1\,M$ methanoic acid to give a solution of pH = 4? (K_a for methanoic acid $= 2.14 \times 10^{-6}$). What would be the pH of this solution on the addition of (a) 1 cm^3 and (b) 5 cm^3 of $0.1\,M$ hydrochloric acid to 1 dm^3 of this buffer solution?

6. Write the equilibrium constant for the hydrolysis of ammonium chloride. Magnesium gives hydrogen gas when added to ammonium chloride solution but not with water. Why?

7. An indicator changes colour at a pH of 2.5, being red below this value and yellow at a higher pH. The dissociation constants for methanoic, ethanoic and benzoic acids are 2.1×10^{-4}, 1.8×10^{-5} and 6.0×10^{-5} respectively. What is the colour of the indicator in a $0.1\,M$ solution of each acid?

8. Hydrogen and iodine react endothermically at room temperature ($\Delta H = +53.8$ kJ mol^{-1}). What conditions would be most likely to favour the formation of hydrogen iodide?

9. The table below gives the pH values during the separate titrations of two acids A and B against sodium hydroxide solution.
   (a) Draw the titration curves.
   (b) Name a suitable indicator in each case.
   (c) Classify A and B as either weak or strong.
   (d) If 20.00 cm^3 portions of the acids (both $0.100\,M$) are used, what is the molarity of the sodium hydroxide solution?

Volume of alkali/cm^3	pH	
	A	B
13.00	1.70	4.95
14.00	1.75	5.05
15.00	1.85	5.20
16.00	2.00	5.35
17.00	2.10	5.55
18.00	2.30	5.70
19.00	2.60	6.00
19.50	2.90	6.90
20.00	7.00	8.90
20.50	11.10	11.05
21.00	11.40	11.70
22.00	11.75	12.00
23.00	11.95	12.10
24.00	12.00	12.25
25.00	12.05	12.30

Part 4

Organic chemistry

Chapter 15

Structure in organic chemistry

The study of organic chemistry began as the study of chemicals occurring in the living systems: in animals and plants. These were compounds based on carbon, hydrogen and oxygen. Nowadays it is the study of similar compounds, but not necessarily those originating from living systems. It is sometimes called 'carbon chemistry', that is the chemistry of compounds of carbon.

Carbon is a unique element in many respects — it occurs in two very different forms: graphite (a soft, black, lubricating solid which is able to conduct electricity) and diamond (colourless, hard and non-conducting). Also carbon is able to bond to itself to give long, strong chains. Most elements that show any ability to bond their atoms to form short chains are only able to form short chains. The bonds between carbon and hydrogen are also exceptionally strong (see Table 15.1). Carbon shows an uncommon ability to form compounds of very different stereochemistries — tetrahedral (sp_3 hybridisation), trigonal planar (sp_2 hybridisation) and linear (sp hybridisation).

Sources of organic chemicals

While organic chemicals do occur widely in living systems, this is not, in general, a good industrial source of useful chemicals. However, coal is used

Table 15.1 Some average bond energies

Bond	Bond energy/ kJ mol^{-1}	Bond	Bond energy/ kJ mol^{-1}
C—C	346	C—H	413
Si—Si	220	Si—H	318
N—N	163	N—H	389
P—P	201	P—H	322
F—F	158	F—H	565
Cl—Cl	242	Cl—H	431

not only as a fuel, but as a raw material for the production of essential compounds. The most widely used source of organic compounds is petroleum oil.

Petroleum oil is a mixture of a large number of hydrocarbons (i.e. compounds composed of carbon and hydrogen only). It is generally believed that oil was formed in nature by the application of heat and pressure to dead organic matter. Recent research has considered the possibility of producing oil rather more rapidly in view of the diminishing natural resources. One

Table 15.2 Distillation of oil

	Boiling temperature of fraction	Fraction name	Hydrocarbon content	Uses
Crude oil	<20	Gas	C_1–C_4	Heating
	20–60	Light petroleum	C_5–C_6	Solvent
	60–100	Ligroin	C_6–C_7	Solvent
	40–205	Petrol	C_5–C_{12}	Fuel for internal combustion engines
	175–325	Kerosene	C_{12}–C_{18}	Heating fuel, jet fuel
	275–400	Gas oil	C_{12}–C_{25}	Heating and diesel fuel
	Non-volatile liquid	Lubricating oil		Paraffin wax (m.p. 50°) Lubrication oil
	Residue	Asphalt or bitumen		Road 'tar'

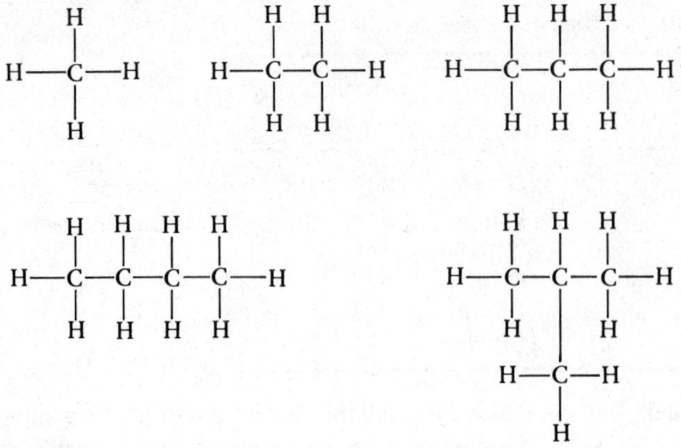

198

Fig. 15.1 Some simple alkanes

report describes its production from cellulose waste (e.g. wood) in 20 minutes. A form of coal was obtained by the U.S. Bureau of Mines by heating wood at a moderate temperature (500 K). If wood is heated under pressure with water, an alkali and carbon monoxide, oil is produced within a few minutes. Some do-it-yourself oil producers have produced oil and gas in their garden sheds by modifications of this process! Other reports suggest that oil is still being produced in substantial quantities through geological disturbances.

Before oil can be used for the production of useful chemicals, it has to be

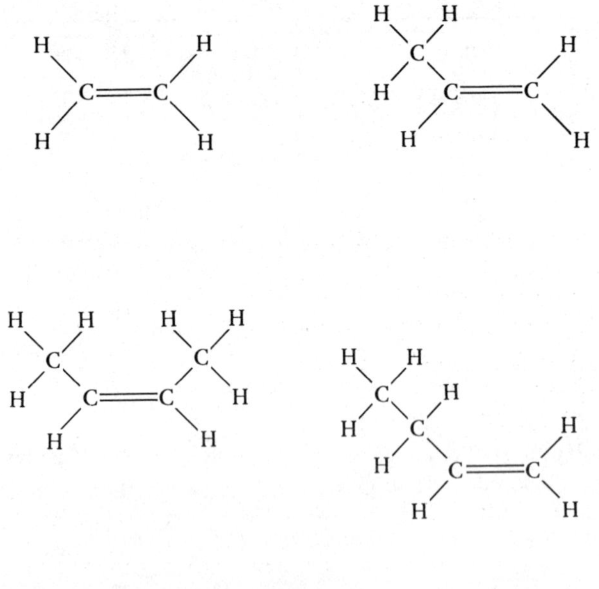

Fig. 15.2 Some simple alkenes

fractionally distilled in order to separate the hydrocarbons into smaller groups. Table 15.2 illustrates the initial separation.

Often the higher boiling fractions are more abundant than demand requires. Conversely, the lighter fractions are insufficient for the demand. If the larger molecules can be broken down, then the balance between supply and demand can be redressed. This is possible by the use of heat and a catalyst. The process is known as *catalytic cracking*. Besides the simple hydrocarbons (Fig. 15.1) that contain only single bonds between the carbon atoms, others are formed with double bonds between some of the carbon atoms (Fig. 15.2). These are significant in both the improvement of petrols and as important starting materials for the production of petrochemicals. Hydrocarbons containing single bonds only are called alkanes; hydrocarbons with double bonds are alkenes.

Petrochemical production

One simple alkene is ethene, C_2H_4. This is a source of several important chemicals such as ethanol:

$$CH_2{=}CH_2 + H_2O \xrightarrow[\substack{\text{Celite} \\ 600\ K,\ 7 \times 10^3\ kPa}]{\text{phosphoric acid}} CH_3CH_2OH;$$

1,2-dichloroethane (a useful solvent):

$$CH_2{=}CH_2 + Cl_2 \xrightarrow[320\ K]{\text{chloride catalyst}} CH_2Cl \cdot CH_2Cl;$$

ethylene oxide (useful for the production of other solvents):

$$CH_2{=}CH_2 + O_2 \xrightarrow[600\ K]{\text{silver}} CH_2{-\!\!\!-}CH_2;$$
$$\diagdown O \diagup$$

vinyl chloride or chloroethene (for the production of the 'plastic' PVC):

$$CH_2{=}CH_2 + Cl_2 \xrightarrow[800\ K]{} CH_2 = CH \cdot Cl;$$

and polyethene:

$$n\,CH_2{=}CH_2 \xrightarrow[\text{heat, pressure}]{\text{catalyst}} {\sim}CH_2 \cdot CH_2{-\!\!\!-}CH_2 \cdot CH_2{\sim}$$

In the last case a variety of catalysts and conditions can be used:

ICI high pressure process	trace of oxygen, 500 K, 1.5×10^5 kPa
Ziegler process	$TiCl_4$–$Al(C_2H_5)_3$, 320–350 K, 200–700 kPa
Phillips process	SiO_2–Al_2O_3, 420–450 K, 3×10^3 kPa.

The structure of organic molecules is most effectively studied using models. Models, either physical or conceptual, are methods of representing processes or situations which are either too small, or too large, for direct observation and interpretation. They need not be exact replicas of a system, in fact they may only be guesses, 'theories', as to what is happening. If they are successful in helping us to explain observations or predict new situations, then they are good working models.

For a study of structure we normally use 'ball and spring' models. Each ball represents an element, different elements being distinguished by different colours (black for carbon, white for hydrogen, red for oxygen, etc.). Each ball has holes drilled into it, the number of holes indicating the number of bonding electrons, and their positions determined by the Sidgwick—Powell theory (page 24). The atoms are joined by springs to represent covalent bonds. The springs have a degree of flexibility as found in bonds.

We draw methane as in Fig. 15.3(a); attempt to construct a model of this. Your result should be as in Fig. 15.3(b).

$$
\begin{array}{c}
H \\
| \\
H-C-H \\
| \\
H
\end{array}
\qquad\qquad
\begin{array}{c}
H \\
| \\
C \\
H \diagup\ |\ \diagdown H \\
H
\end{array}
$$

Fig. 15.3 Structure of methane

We use a convention in diagrams to illustrate a three-dimensional effect. If a pair of atoms lies in the plane of the paper, the bond is shown as a narrow line (————); when one atom comes out from the plane of the paper, a wedge-shaped line is used (——◀), the wider end indicating that the atom is protruding from the paper; a dotted line is used for a bond receding into the paper.

Ethane has the formula C_2H_6. Using the relevant balls and a supply of springs, join these atoms together and draw the model. You should find that the molecule can only be formed if the carbon atoms are joined together (C—C) and then three hydrogens are attached to each carbon (Fig. 15.4(a)).

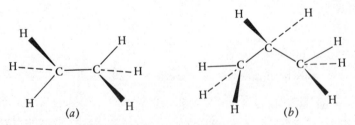

Fig. 15.4 Models of (a) ethane and (b) propane

Similarly a model of propane (C_3H_8) is as shown in Fig. 15.4(*b*)).
Although we often draw the molecule as

$$\begin{array}{ccccccc}
& H & & H & & H & \\
& | & & | & & | & \\
H- & C & - & C & - & C & -H \\
& | & & | & & | & \\
& H & & H & & H &
\end{array}$$

and call it a 'straight chain' molecule (in contrast to a 'branched chain' or a 'cyclic' molecule), we note that the molecule is, in fact, bent. Now construct C_4H_{10}. You should be able to make two different structures (Fig. 15.5). Model (*a*) is a 'straight chain' molecule; model (*b*) is a 'branched chain' molecule — one or more carbons are branched off the main chain. Notice also another important factor — it is possible to rotate the model (*a*) to get an

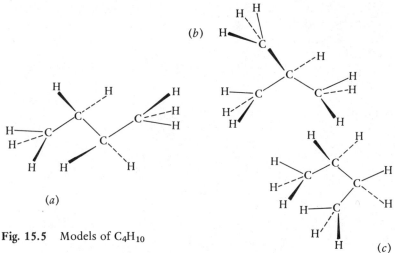

Fig. 15.5   Models of C_4H_{10}

apparently different arrangement (Fig. 15.5(*c*)). Since these can be interconverted by simple rotation without breaking any bonds, they are the same substance. The two forms (*a*) and (*c*) are drawn in two dimensions as

$$\begin{array}{ccccccccc}
& H & & H & & H & & H & \\
& | & & | & & | & & | & \\
H- & C & - & C & - & C & - & C & -H \\
& | & & | & & | & & | & \\
& H & & H & & H & & H &
\end{array}
\qquad
\begin{array}{ccccccc}
& H & & H & & H & \\
& | & & | & & | & \\
H- & C & - & C & - & C & -H \\
& | & & | & & | & \\
& H & & H & & H & \\
& & & & & | & \\
& & & & H- & C & -H \\
& & & & & | & \\
& & & & & H &
\end{array}$$

In this format we must look for the continuous chains rather than straight lines. The models (*a*) and (*c*) are called *conformers;* (*a*) and (*b*), or (*c*) and (*b*), are called *isomers.*

Conformers are identical molecules formed by rotation about bonds and are usually indistinguishable physically and chemically, and they coexist in a compound.

Isomers are different molecules formed by the breaking of bonds and forming of new bonds; they are normally separable and distinct in their properties.

Nomenclature

It is now possible for us to understand how organic compounds are named.

1. Find the longest continuous chain of carbon atoms, e.g.

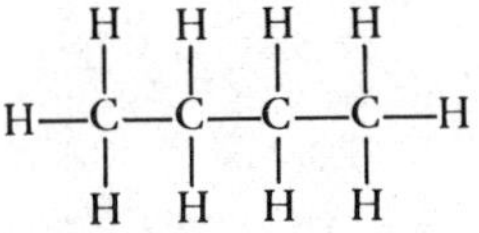

and

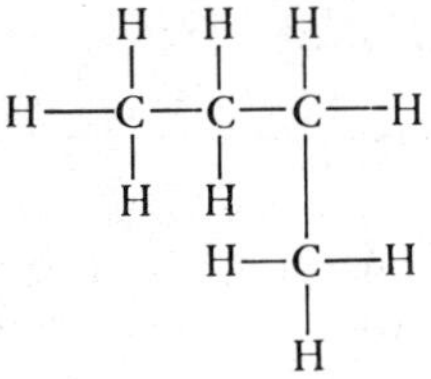

both have

continuous chains of four carbon atoms;

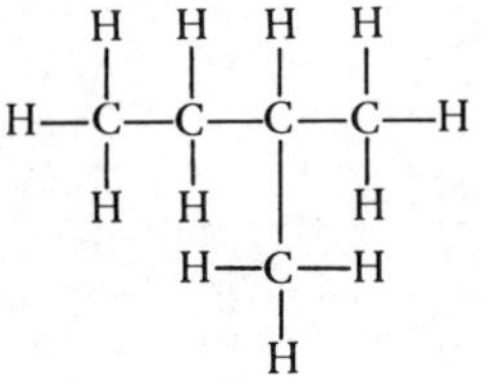

also has a continuous chain of four

carbon atoms;

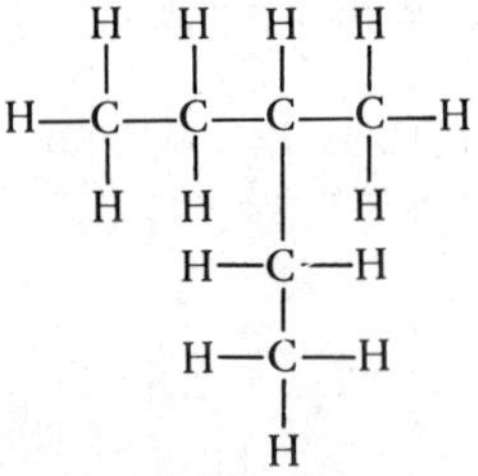

has a longest continuous chain of five

carbon atoms.

2. The main stem to the name is determined by *this* number of carbon atoms (Table 15.3).

Table 15.3 Nomenclature of organic compounds 203

No. of carbon atoms in longest continuous chain	Stem of the name
1	meth
2	eth
3	prop
4	but
5	pent
6	hex
7	hept
8	oct
9	non
10	dec

3. Add, as a suffix, 'an' if the carbon atoms are joined by single bonds only. If there is no further suffix (e.g. no atoms other than hydrogen are present) the name ends with 'e'. So, for example,

C_2H_6 is ethane,
C_3H_8 is propane,
and

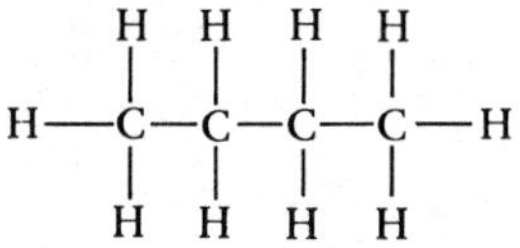

$$H-\underset{\underset{H}{|}}{\overset{\overset{H}{|}}{C}}-\underset{\underset{H}{|}}{\overset{\overset{H}{|}}{C}}-\underset{\underset{H}{|}}{\overset{\overset{H}{|}}{C}}-\underset{\underset{H}{|}}{\overset{\overset{H}{|}}{C}}-H \qquad \text{is butane.}$$

4. Locate, name and identify the position of any branch groupings. For example,

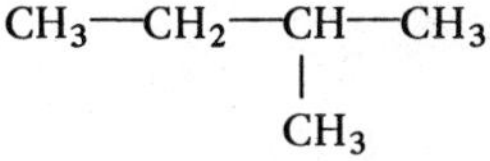

$$CH_3-CH_2-\underset{\underset{CH_3}{|}}{CH}-CH_3$$

has a chain of four carbon atoms and so is a butane. There is a one carbon branch chain. The chain is called methyl: 'meth' for the single carbon atom and 'yl' to indicate that it is a group added as a side-chain. It is on the second carbon of the chain; it could be considered to be the third carbon from the opposite end, but it is conventional to use the smallest number for the position. This is, therefore, named 2-methylbutane.

What is the name of the following compound?

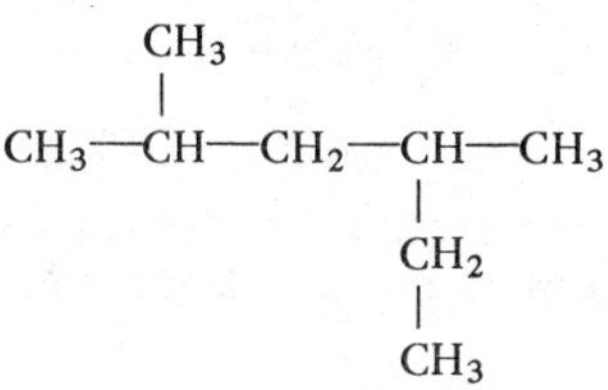

$$CH_3-\underset{\underset{\underset{\underset{CH_3}{|}}{\underset{CH_2}{|}}}{\overset{\overset{CH_3}{|}}{CH}}}-CH_2-\underset{\underset{\underset{\underset{CH_3}{|}}{CH_2}}{|}}{CH}-CH_3$$

The longest continuous chain is of six carbons joined by single bonds (hexane); there are two branching groups, both are methyl groups, and they are in positions 2 and 4. So, the name is 2,4-dimethylhexane. Note that we combine the two similar groups by using the prefix di-. (Similarly, three would be prefixed by tri-, four by tetra-, etc.) The position numbers are separated by commas from each other and by hyphens from the names.

Multiple bonds

Construct a model of ethene (C_2H_4) and draw it. What contrasts do you notice between ethene and ethane? Figure 15.6 shows the result you should obtain. The six atoms all lie in one plane. The nomenclature is determined in the same manner as for the alkanes. The stem of the name is determined by the number of carbon atoms in the continuous chain (page 203). The suffix 'en' is used if a double bond is present. So, $CH_2\!\!=\!\!CH_2$ is ethene and $CH_3\!\!-\!\!CH\!\!=\!\!CH_2$ is propene. In the longer chains there are alternative positions for the double bond; the double bond position is then indicated by specifying the position at which the bond begins. The butenes are named but-1-ene ($CH_3 \cdot CH_2 \cdot CH\!\!=\!\!CH_2$) and but-2-ene ($CH_3 \cdot CH\!\!=\!\!CH \cdot CH_3$).

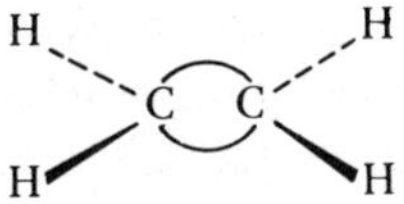

Fig. 15.6   Structure of ethene

Carbon can form triple bonds as in $H\!\!-\!\!C\!\!\equiv\!\!C\!\!-\!\!H$. The suffix 'yn' is used to indicate the presence of the triple bond. This compound is, therefore, ethyne. Propyne is $CH_3\!\!-\!\!C\!\!\equiv\!\!CH$.

Cyclic compounds

So far we have considered compounds involving 'straight' or 'branched' chains. It is also possible to have cyclic molecules. Construct a molecule based on a ring of six carbon atoms (with single bonds only) and add the appropriate number of hydrogen atoms. What is the formula of the molecule? Are there any conformers of this compound?

The molecular formula of this compound is C_6H_{12} and its two conformers are shown in Fig. 15.7. The nomenclature is as for the alkanes with the prefix 'cyclo': cyclohexane (cyclo − ring, hex − six carbon chain, an − single bonds only).

Now introduce a double bond into the ring (C_6H_{10}). What is the effect? See Fig. 15.8. Alkenes are planar molecules (see above). The introduction of a double bond into the cyclic system causes the carbon atoms 1–4 (Fig. 15.8) to lie in one plane.

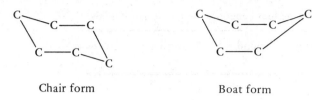

Chair form   Boat form

Fig. 15.7 Conformers of cyclohexane
(hydrogen atoms are omitted for clarity)

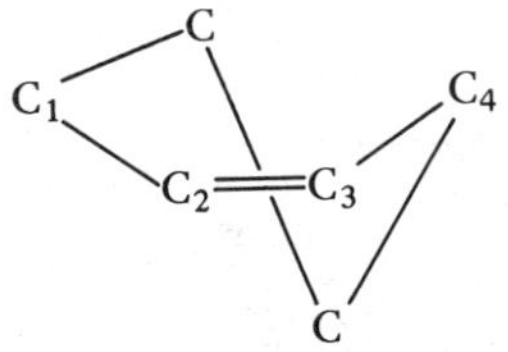

Fig. 15.8 Structure of cyclohexene (hydrogens omitted)

Figure 15.9 shows the structure of a six-carbon ring with three double bonds. It could be named as cyclohexatriene, but because of its unusual properties (see page 218), it is given a special name: benzene. Notice the complete loss of flexibility in this structure. It is a member of a series of such compounds, e.g. methylbenzene (also known as toluene; Fig. 15.9).

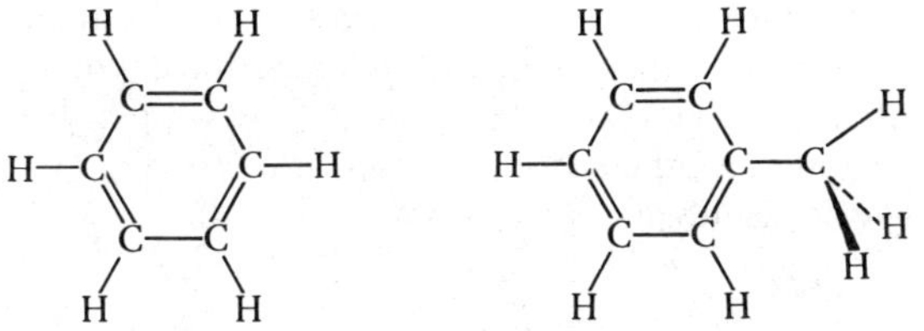

Fig. 15.9 Structure of benzene and methylbenzene

Functional groups

We have already noted the general stability of C—C and C—H bonds. If organic compounds are to possess a general reactivity, they must have other weaker bonds present. Table 15.4 lists some carbon bond energies.

It will be noticed that, other than the C—F bond, the single bonds (C—O, C—Cl, C—Br, C—I, C—N) are weaker than the C—H bonds. Also, in the multiple-bonded compounds, the second and third bonds are weaker than the first single bond (except C=O); e.g. in C=C, the bond energy can be considered as $(346 + 265) = 611$ kJ mol^{-1}. So, as a general rule, we can say that atoms or groups attached to the carbon atoms are more weakly held, and

Table 15.4 Some average bond energies in organic compounds

Bond	Bond energy/ kJ mol^{-1}	Bond	Bond energy/ kJ mol^{-1}
C—C	346	C—F	452
C=C	611	C—Cl	339
C≡C	835	C—Br	209
C—H	413	C—I	218
C—O	358	C—N	305
C=O	740	C=N	615
		C≡N	890

so are more susceptible to attack, than C——C or C——H bonds. Consequently, we are able to discuss the chemistry of these groups rather than the carbon backbone to the molecule. These reactive groups are known as *functional groups*. For example,

$$CH_3 — CH — COOH$$
$$\qquad\quad |$$
$$\qquad\quad NH_2$$

is naturally-occurring molecule which is involved in proteins. Its chemistry is determined by the basic group, NH_2, and the acidic group, COOH.

The functional group names (Table 15.5) can be added as either prefixes or suffixes to the stem. If several groups are present, then they are listed in alphabetical order. The suffix is used in preference to a prefix. Where there are alternative possible suffixes, due to the presence of two functional groups, the order of priority is that given in Table 15.5; the groups with higher priority are suffixed to the name, the others are introduced as prefixes.

Consider the following compounds and their names.

C_2H_5Br	bromoethane
CH_3OH	methanol (or hydroxymethane)
$CH_3CH_2NH_2$	ethanamine (or aminoethane)
$CH_3CH_2CH_2CN$	butanenitrile (the 'e' is retained in the name because of the ease in pronunciation; note that *all* the carbons are to be included in the name)
CH_3CH_2COOH	propanoic acid
$CH_3CH_2OCH_3$	methoxyethane (remember that the stem uses the longest chain)

$$CH_3—CH—CH_3 \qquad \text{propan-2-ol (or 2-hydroxypropane)}$$
$$\qquad\quad |$$
$$\qquad\quad OH$$

$Cl \cdot CH_2CH_2OH$	2-chloroethanol
CH_3CHO	ethanal
CH_3COCH_3	propanone

Since the reactivity of a compound is independent of the unreactive

Table 15.5   Suffixes and prefixes for functional group nomenclature   207

Formula	Group name	Prefix	Suffix
COOH	carboxylic acid	—	oic acid
SO_3H	sulphonic acid	sulpho	sulphonic acid
COOR	ester	—	alkyl . . . cate
COX	acyl halide	—	oyl halide
$CONH_2$	amide	—	amide
CN	nitrile	—	nitrile
CHO	aldehyde	oxo	al
CO	ketone	oxo	one
OH	alcohol	hydroxy	ol
NH_2	amine	amino	amine
Cl, Br, I	halide	halogeno	—
OR	ether	alkyloxy*	—
SH	thiol	mercapto	thiol

(*alkoxy is used for C_1–C_4)

carbon skeleton and is determined solely by the functional group, the organic compounds can be divided into series which have the same properties. For example, the alcohols are a series of compounds containing the hydroxy group (OH) attached to a carbon skeleton. Consider the following set of alcohols:

CH_3OH	methanol
CH_3CH_2OH	ethanol
$CH_3CH_2CH_2OH$	propan-1-ol
$CH_3CH_2CH_2CH_2OH$	butan-1-ol

In this series the length of the chain is gradually increased; the members of this series have identical chemical properties and differ from each other only by CH_2. This is an *homologous series*: a series of compounds which have a regular structural pattern and similar chemical properties, each member of which differs from its neighbouring members by a CH_2 group only.

Organic quantitative analysis

In organic compounds the most commonly occurring elements are carbon, hydrogen and oxygen; nitrogen, sulphur and the halogens (e.g. chlorine) also occur frequently. The basic step in the quantitative analysis of an organic compound is the complete oxidation of the compound to carbon dioxide, water, nitrogen, sulphate ions and halide ions. Oxygen is not normally determined directly.

The carbon and hydrogen are oxidised by oxygen in the presence of hot copper(II) oxide. The carbon dioxide is determined by absorption by alkali;

water is absorbed by anhydrous calcium chloride. Oxidation by fuming nitric acid converts covalent sulphur to sulphate and liberates the halide ions. These are precipitated as barium sulphate and silver halide respectively. The nitrogen is generated by oxidation of the organic material using copper(II) oxide in the absence of air; the resultant gases are passed over heated copper to reduce any oxides of nitrogen to molecular nitrogen. The gas is collected over alkaline solution (to remove acidic gases) and the volume is measured. An alternative method for the estimation of nitrogen is to convert it to ammonia and determine the amount by titration.

Each of these results will give a percentage of the element in the original compound. For example, 27.29 per cent of the carbon dioxide is carbon (12.011 g carbon in 44.009 g CO_2); 11.19 per cent of water is hydrogen (2.016 g hydrogen in 18.015 g water); sulphur is 13.74 per cent of the barium sulphate (32.06 g sulphur in 233.40 g barium sulphate); there is 24.74 per cent chlorine in any silver chloride precipitated (35.45 g chlorine per 143.32 g AgCl); nitrogen is 82.25 per cent of the ammonia collected (14.007 g nitrogen in 17.03 g ammonia).

For example, if 0.228 g carbon dioxide was obtained on oxidation of 0.100 g of an organic compound, then we can determine the amount of carbon in the carbon dioxide as 27.29 per cent of 0.228 g = 0.062 22 g. The percentage of carbon in the organic material is (0.062 22/0.100) × 100 per cent = 62.22 per cent.

Once the percentages of the elements are known, it is possible to determine the ratio of the atoms present, that is the *empirical formula*. If the percentages do not add up to 100 per cent (within experimental error), it is assumed that the balance is oxygen.

Consider a compound which is found to contain 62.22 per cent carbon and 10.35 per cent hydrogen. The amount of oxygen must be

$100 - (62.22 + 10.35) = 27.43$ per cent

The ratio of atoms in the molecule is obtained from the quotient of the percentage and the corresponding relative atomic masses (only a ratio is possible since the relative atomic masses are themselves relative values). Since

Elements	Carbon		Hydrogen		Oxygen
Percentages:	62.22		10.35		27.43
Relative atomic masses	12.01		1.008		16.00
Ratio of atoms:	$\dfrac{62.22}{12.01}$	:	$\dfrac{10.35}{1.008}$	:	$\dfrac{27.43}{16.00}$
	= 5.181	:	10.27	:	1.714
	= 3.023	:	5.992	:	1.000

molecules contain whole numbers of atoms, the empirical formula is obtained by dividing through by the smallest percentage (in this case, 1.714). So, the

ratio is 3.02 C, 5.99 H, 1.00 O, which within experimental error is C_3H_6O.
But, remember, $C_6H_{12}O_2$ would give the same percentages. We need to know the relative molecular mass of the compound to decide on the true number of atoms.

Properties

(a) Melting point
The melting points are dependent on the relative molecular masses, chain branching, polarity and hydrogen-bonding. For linear molecules with no polarity, the melting point increases with the relative molecular mass. Chain branching hinders ease of packing into a crystal and so melting occurs more readily, i.e. at a lower temperature than for the straight chain molecules. C_4H_8 represents butane (m.p. $-138°C$) and 2-methylpropane (m.p. $-160°C$). Molecules with polar groupings have higher melting points since more energy is required to break intermolecular forces. For example, propane (relative molecular mass 44) has m.p. $-188°C$ and propene (42) has m.p. $-185°C$, but ethanol (46) has a m.p. of $-117°C$. Methoxymethane (46) has an intermediate polarity and a m.p. of $-139°C$. With the larger molecules, due to the flexibility of the chains preventing strong hydrogen-bonding, the difference between the alkanes and alcohols is less substantial.

(b) Solubility
The solubility of organic compounds follows the rules given on page 38. Basically 'like dissolves like'; non-polar covalent compounds are soluble in non-polar covalent solvents and polar solvents dissolve polar compounds. So, the alcohols are miscible with water and propanone (acetone). Hydrocarbons are immiscible with water, but miscible with benzene, for example.

(c) Reactivity
Chemical reactivity is determined by bond energy and polarity or polarisability of bonds. For example, in the halogenoalkanes the carbon—fluorine bonds are very strong (see Table 15.4) and so fluoroalkanes are very unreactive. The chlorocompounds have weaker bonds and so are more susceptible to attack; and the bromoalkanes are even more easily affected by chemical reagents.

The position of attack is determined by the polarity of a bond. For example, in the chloroalkanes the carbon atom is positively charged with

$$-\overset{|}{\underset{|}{C}}{}^{\delta+}-Cl^{\delta-}$$

respect to the chlorine. A negatively charged reagent, e.g. OH^-, will cause attack on the carbon. The less the polarity, the less the chance of reaction.

Some groups are susceptible to attack because of the ease with which the electron distribution is disturbed. The multiple-bonded systems C=C and

$C{=}O$ have high bond energies. These are, however, reactive groups. When approached by a positive reagent, the electron density of the π-bond can be distorted:

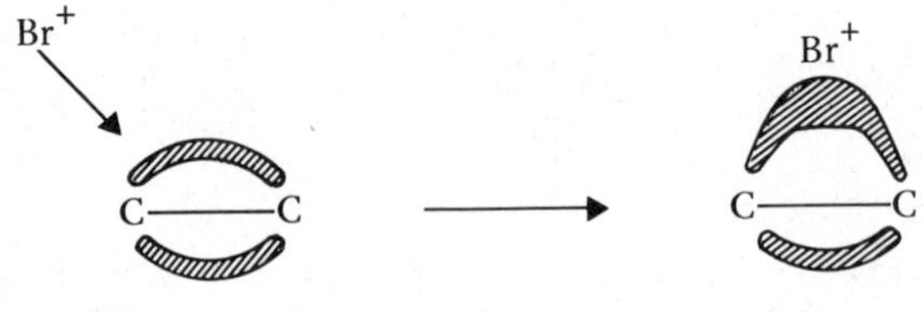

This causes a reduction in the electron density on the carbon and allows the formation of a relative positive charge:

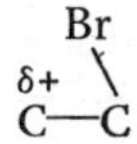

$$\overset{\delta+}{C}\!\!-\!\!\overset{\overset{\displaystyle Br}{\big|}}{C}$$

This distortion of the electron density is known as *polarisation* (though the word is the same, it does not have the same meaning as in electrochemistry, page 140), and the ease of distortion is the *polarisability* of the bond.

(d) Colour

Most organic compounds are colourless. Some species are intensely coloured – dyestuffs and chlorophyll, for example. The criterion for colour is the presence of a conjugated system. This can be either a very long conjugated system or a shorter one with an atom possessing non-bonding pairs of electrons. A *conjugated* system is one which consists of alternate single and double bonds between the atoms. For example, a simple dyestuff is the molecule *para*-hydroxyazobenzene:

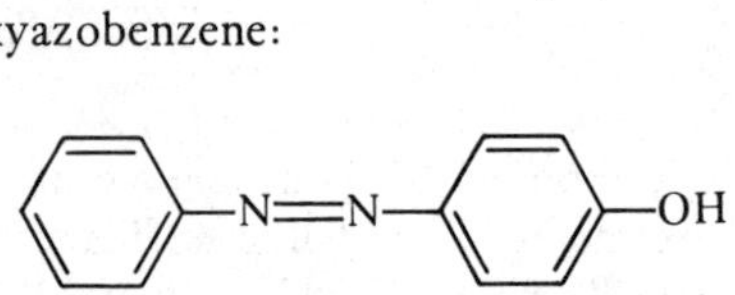

This has seven double bonds with alternating single bonds; it also contains nitrogen atoms which have non-bonding electrons. Carotene is a red pigment occurring in such plants as carrots and tomatoes; it does not include the atoms such as nitrogen, but it does have a very long conjugated chain:

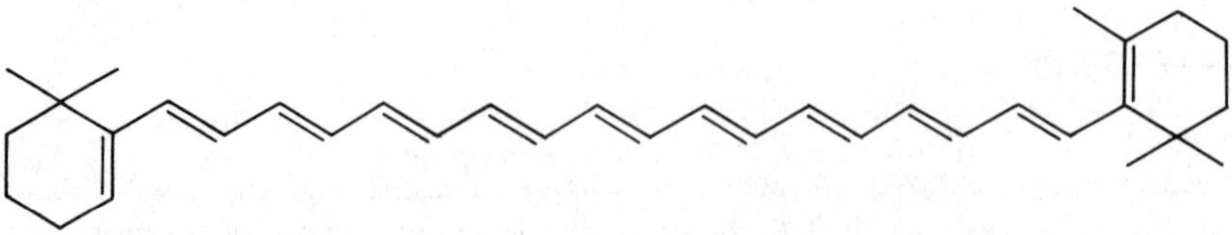

Chlorophyll contains a porphyrin unit attached to magnesium:

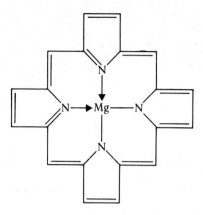

Various groups are attached around the ring, but the conjugated system shown is the critical unit. A similar unit is attached to iron to give haem, the active component of red blood cells. Similarly, vitamin B_{12} contains porphyrin linked to cobalt.

This chapter has described the structure and general properties of organic compounds. It has introduced the functional groups and their nomenclature. The final chapter shows how the chemical properties of these carbon derivatives can be predicted by the identification of the reactive groups.

Summary

At the conclusion of this chapter, you should be able to:

1. state how carbon is unique chemically;
2. describe how oil is used as a source of useful hydrocarbon mixtures;
3. state that alkenes are obtained from hydrocarbons by catalytic cracking;
4. describe reactions in which ethene is converted to useful chemicals;
5. recognise that saturated carbon compounds are tetrahedral in arrangement;
6. recognise that structures interconverted by rotation about a bond are conformers of the same substance;
7. know that structures with the same molecular formula and interconverted by breaking bonds are called isomers;
8. name a hydrocarbon from its structural formula;
9. know what is meant by a functional group;
10. name an organic compound containing a functional group;
11. state which factors affect the melting point of an organic substance;
12. state that polar covalent compounds dissolve in polar solvents;
13. recognise centres of polarity as positions most susceptible to chemical attack;

14. describe a conjugated system as one consisting of alternate single and double bonds;
15. state that coloured compounds involve conjugated systems;
16. calculate the percentages of elements present in organic compounds from analytical data.

Experiments

1. Construct models representing molecules of different stereochemistries.
2. Distil crude oil, collecting various fractions.
3. Crack a petroleum fraction and test for unsaturation.
4. Measure the boiling points of an homologous series, plotting the relative molecular mass against the boiling point.
5. Examine the ultraviolet/visible spectra of a selection of aromatic compounds in order to determine the effect of functional groups and conjugation on light absorption.
6. Organic analysis (*Selected Experiments in Physical Science;* D. H. Marrow (Longman, 1974) Ch. 11).

References

The physical and chemical properties of petrol; R. Oxtoby, *Sch. Sci. Rev.,* 1972, **53**, 509—19.
An introduction to the chemistry of oil refining (Esso).
Chemicals — manufacture and applications (Shell).
Petroleum chemicals (B.P.)
Acetic acid from aliphatic hydrocarbons (D.C.L.).
Phenol by the cumene route (D.C.L.).

Films

The chemistry of oil (B.P.).
Acetic acid achievement (B.P.).

Filmloop

Organic analysis by mass spectrometer (Nuffield, Longman).

Questions

1. Draw the structures of the following compounds:
   (a) 2-methylbut-2-ene; (b) 2-chloropropanoic acid; (c) 2,2-dichloro-

propanol; (d) 3-hydroxybutanoic acid; (e) propanone; (f) 1-methoxy-
propane; (g) propyl methanoate; (h) cyclohexanamine; (i) 1,3-butadiene;
(j) 1-iodobut-2-yne.

2. Name the following compounds:

(a) $CH_3 \cdot CH(OH)CH_3$; (b) $CH_3 \cdot CH(NH_2) \cdot COOH$; (c) $CH_3 \cdot CH_2 \cdot CN$;

(d) $CCl_3 \cdot CHO$; (e) $CH_3{-}CH{-}Br$; (f)
$$CH_3{-}CH{-}Br$$
with CH_2 and CH_3 substituents

$$\underset{CH_3}{\underset{|}{\underset{CH_2}{\underset{|}{CH_3{-}CH{-}Br}}}}; \quad (f)\ \underset{CH_3}{\underset{|}{CH_3{-}CH_2{-}\overset{H}{\overset{|}{C}}{-}CH_3}};$$

(g) $CH_3{-}CH{=}CH{-}\underset{CH_3}{\underset{|}{CH_2}}$; (h) $(CH_3)_2CH \cdot CHO$.

3. Consider an organic compound with the formula:

(a) Is the compound likely to be soluble in water?
(b) Would you expect it to be coloured or colourless?
(c) Which parts of the molecule are most susceptible to chemical attack by a polar reagent?
(d) How flexible is the structure? Can you draw any conformers?
(e) Draw an isomer of this compound.
Give your reasons for your answers.

4. 0.331 g of an organic substance on combustion gave 0.176 g carbon dioxide and 0.054 g water. Another sample, 0.463 g, gave 1.204 g of silver chloride after oxidation and treatment with silver nitrate solution. Determine the percentages of carbon, hydrogen, chlorine and oxygen in the substance and hence its empirical formula. How would you attempt to determine the molecular formula?

Chapter 16

Reactions in organic chemistry

Combustion

A general property of organic compounds is their combustibility. Hydrocarbons, from petroleum oil, burn and they are widely used as fuels:

$CH_4 + 2O_2 \rightarrow CO_2 + 2H_2O$, $\Delta H = -890$ kJ mol^{-1}
$C_2H_4 + 3O_2 \rightarrow 2CO_2 + 2H_2O$, $\Delta H = -1411$ kJ mol^{-1}
$C_6H_6 + 7\frac{1}{2}O_2 \rightarrow 6CO_2 + 3H_2O$, $\Delta H = -3268$ kJ mol^{-1}

Other compounds are also potential fuels, giving out heat when burnt:

$CH_3OH + 1\frac{1}{2}O_2 \rightarrow CO_2 + 2H_2O$, $\Delta H = -726$ kJ mol^{-1}
$C_2H_5OH + 3O_2 \rightarrow 2CO_2 + 3H_2O$, $\Delta H = -1367$ kJ mol^{-1}
$CH_3OCH_3 + 3O_2 \rightarrow 2CO_2 + 3H_2O$, $\Delta H = -1454$ kJ mol^{-1}.

Some compounds, particularly the more lighly halogenated compounds, are less efficient fuels.

Reduction

A variety of reducing agents is available for use in organic chemistry, but reduction can be classified into three main types:

1. hydrogen with a catalyst;
2. active metals and a solvent;
3. complex metal hydrides.

1. Catalytic hydrogenation is normally performed using nickel as a catalyst under fairly mild conditions. Palladium and platinum are alternatives, but are expensive and more easily poisoned by impurities, so losing their catalytic activity. It is a method of reduction particularly suitable for use with unsaturated compounds — that is compounds which have multiple bonds and so are able to accept new atoms or groups without the simultaneous displacement of other groups. Alkenes are converted to alkanes; nitriles, oximes and other multiple-bonded carbon—nitrogen compounds give amines, as do nitro compounds; carbonyl compounds give alcohols.

2. The use of active metals involves an electron transfer system. (This process was formerly described as a 'nascent hydrogen' reduction, but the hydrogen is not the reducing species.) In these systems, a metal is dissolved in a protoic solvent (that is a solvent yielding solvated protons on dissociation) and the compound is reduced by this reagent *in situ*. A variety of metals and solvents is used, depending on the strength of reducing agent required:

Zn—acid   Na—alcohol   Na—liquid ammonia

$$\xrightarrow{\hspace{4cm}}$$

increasing reducing power

The process is one in which electrons are released by the metal

$$M \to M^{n+} + n\,e^{-}$$

and are taken up by either a proton from the solvent

$$H^{+} + e^{-} \to \tfrac{1}{2}H_2$$

or by an organic molecule

$$e^{-} + CR_2{=}O + H^{+} \to {}^{-}CR_2 \cdot OH \xrightarrow{H^{+}} HCR_2 \cdot OH$$

(the curved arrows show the direction of electron movement).

3. The third group of reagents are the complex hydrides, such as lithium aluminium hydride (or lithium tetrahydroaluminate). This must be used in an inert organic solvent since it reacts with protoic solvents. It reduces a large range of compounds (see Table 16.1) by attacking (through the AlH_4^{-} ion) a polar centre in the molecule. Other related hydrides are known, for example, sodium borohydride ($NaBH_4$). This is much more selective; for example, it does not affect carboxylic acids, nitriles or nitro compounds, all of which are attacked by lithium aluminium hydride. Lithium aluminium hydride is a difficult and dangerous substance to handle. It is of low density and the powder is easily inhaled; it reacts readily with moisture; it is pyrophoric and toxic. A more suitable hydride is a partially substituted compound sodium

$$Na[AlH_2(OCH_2CH_2OCH_3)_2]$$

dihydrobis(2-methoxyethoxyaluminate) which is sold under such trade names as 'Red-Al'. The advantage of this reagent is that the introduction of the ether

Table 16.1 Complex hydride reducing agents

Substrate	Product for		
	$LiAlH_4$	$NaBH_4$	$LiAlH_4-Al_2Cl_6$
Carbonyls	alcohols	alcohols	hydrocarbons
Acyl chlorides	alcohols	alcohols	alcohols
Acids	alcohols	–	hydrocarbons
Nitriles	aldehydes	–	amines
Esters	alcohols	–	alcohols
Amides	amines	amines	amines
Nitroalkanes	amines	–	amines
Halogenoalkanes	–	–	alkanes
Epoxides	–	–	alcohols

grouping to the anion enhances its solubility in organic solvents (it is usually purchased in solution) and yet retains the reactivity of the parent species. It is possible to alter the reactivity of these hydrides with the use of aluminium choride (Al_2Cl_6) as a subsidiary catalyst.

The general properties of the various homologous series are discussed in the rest of the chapter.

Alkanes

There are only two bond types in these compounds: C—C and C—H. As mentioned in Chapter 15, these are strong bonds and so the alkanes are not very reactive. The only reaction (aside from combustion) is substitution for hydrogen. This is best illustrated in the chlorination of an alkane. When an alkane is mixed with chlorine in ultraviolet light, or at a temperature of $250°-400°C$, a series of substitution reactions occurs. The reaction is initiated by the dissociation of chlorine molecules into atoms

$$Cl_2 \xrightarrow{u.v.} 2Cl \cdot$$

These atoms are very reactive and are able to attack the C—H bonds

$$CH_4 + Cl \cdot \rightarrow CH_3 \cdot + HCl$$
$$CH_3 \cdot + Cl_2 \rightarrow CH_3Cl + Cl \cdot$$

(The dots after the atoms and methyl groups indicate the presence of unpaired electrons.) The reaction is sustained by the continual regeneration of chlorine atoms. Further substitution occurs to give a mixture of products: CH_3Cl (chloromethane), CH_2Cl_2 (dichloromethane), $CHCl_3$ (trichloromethane) and CCl_4 (tetrachloromethane). These are difficult to separate and so the reaction is not used as a means of preparation of halogenated compounds.

Fluorination and bromination also occur by this mechanism. Iodination is not possible.

Alkenes

In contrast to the alkanes, alkenes are easily attacked by a range of reagents. The weakest point, in terms of bond strength, in an alkene is the π-bond.

Table 16.2 Some alkenes and their physical properties

	B.p./$^\circ$C	Enthalpy of formation/ kJ mol^{-1}	Enthalpy of combustion/ kJ mol^{-1}
Ethene	−103.7	+52.3	−1411
Propene	− 47.7	+20.4	−2059
But-1-ene	− 6.3	− 0.1	−2717
Hex-1-ene	63.5	−41.7	−4004
Cyclohexene	83.2		−4128

Chemical reactions occur between this bond and reactive molecules such as bromine and hydrogen bromide:

$H_2C\!=\!\!=\!\!CH_2 + Br_2 \rightarrow CH_2Br\cdot CH_2Br$ (1,2-dibromoethane)
$H_2C\!=\!\!=\!\!CH_2 + HBr \rightarrow CH_3\cdot CH_2\cdot Br$ (bromoethane).

As will be seen from the equations, the reaction is one of addition; nothing is displaced, in contrast to the halogenation of alkanes in which the hydrogen halide is liberated. Compounds which undergo addition reactions are described as unsaturated compounds.

When bromine is added to ethene, 1,2-dibromoethane is produced. The red colour of the bromine is discharged and a colourless oil is formed. This reaction can be used as a test for unsaturation. (To be suitable for use as a test, a reaction must be simple, fairly rapid, specific to a particular compound or group of compounds, and must have an easily detectable change.)

The same principle of addition is applicable to a wide range of reagents: 'bromine water' (the active constituent is HOBr),

$CH_2\!=\!\!=\!\!CH_2 + HOBr \rightarrow CH_2Br\cdot CH_2OH$
$\qquad\qquad\qquad$ 2-bromoethanol

sulphuric acid (which adds H_2SO_4; the sulphate can be displaced by hydrolysis to give an alcohol),

$CH_2\!=\!\!=\!\!CH_2 + H_2SO_4 \rightarrow CH_3\cdot CH_2\cdot HSO_4$
$CH_3\cdot CH_2\cdot HSO_4 + H_2O \rightarrow CH_3\cdot CH_2\cdot OH + H_2SO_4$
$\qquad\qquad\qquad\qquad$ ethanol

potassium permanganate (which by oxidation and hydrolysis adds two OH groups),

$5CH_2\!=\!\!=\!\!CH_2 + 2MnO_4^- + 2H_2O + 6H^+ \rightarrow 5HO\cdot CH_2\cdot CH_2\cdot OH + 2Mn^{2+}$

and hydrogen (with a nickel catalyst).

$CH_2\!=\!\!=\!\!CH_2 + H_2 \rightarrow CH_3\cdot CH_3$

Consider the reaction of bromine with propene. Write the name and formula of the product.

If you examine the reaction, there are two possible products that you could write:

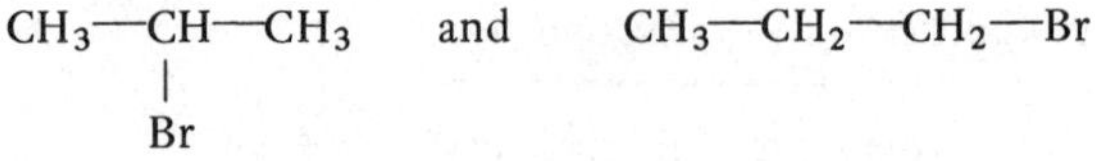

$$CH_3—CH—CH_3 \quad \text{and} \quad CH_3—CH_2—CH_2—Br$$
$$\mid$$
$$Br$$

Analysis of the reaction products shows that only the former compound is produced. This can be shown experimentally to obey the general rule which was first formulated by Markovnikov: In an addition reaction of a molecule of the form HX to an unsymmetrical alkene, the hydrogen atom is attached to the least substituted carbon atom (that is the one with the largest number of hydrogen atoms bonded to it):

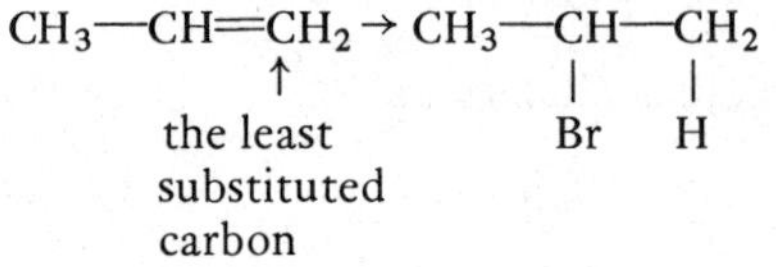

$$CH_3—CH{=}CH_2 \rightarrow CH_3—CH—CH_2$$
$$\uparrow \qquad\qquad \mid \quad \mid$$
$$\text{the least} \qquad Br \quad H$$
$$\text{substituted}$$
$$\text{carbon}$$

Arenes

As seen in Chapter 15, cyclohexatriene is normally called benzene. It is the parent compound of a series of compounds called arenes, or aromatic hydro-carbons. Cyclohexene and cyclohexadiene both display the expected proper-ties of alkenes. Benzene, in contrast, shows very few addition reactions, but several substitution reactions – it behaves like a more reactive alkane! The bonding is formally represented by Fig. 16.1(a). The junctions between two lines, in the short-hand version, are the positions of carbon atoms; hydrogen

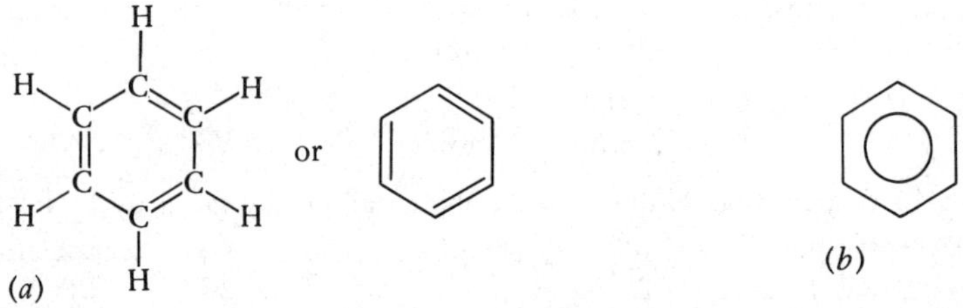

Fig. 16.1 Structure of benzene

atoms are not included unless they are significant to the chemical reactions. This formula suggests that the double bonds are localised between particular pairs of atoms, with single bonds in alternative positions. The chemical properties and physical techniques, such as crystallography, show that the bonds are all equivalent and intermediate between the two extremes (single

and double bonds). The π-bonds, are, therefore, considered to be delocalised
and spread around the molecule. This is represented in the modern formulation of benzene, Fig. 16.1(*b*). The bond length (the distance between the two nuclei) is dependent on the bond order (the number of covalent bonds binding the two atoms together). Figure 16.2 shows the variation in bond

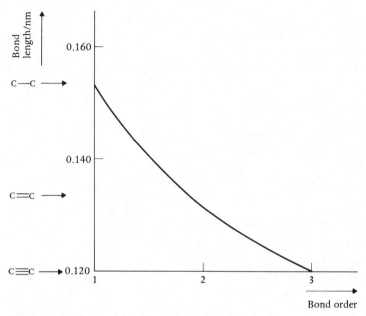

Fig. 16.2   Relationship of bond length to bond order

length with bond order. Benzene is found to have a C—C bond length of 0.139 nm. What is its bond order? A bond length of 0.139 nm corresponds to a bond order of 1.5.

Because of the nature of the π-bonding in these compounds, the chemical properties (see below) are not those normally associated with alkenes. Compounds with this bonding arrangement and these characteristic properties are called *aromatic* compounds. Aromatic compounds are compounds which have delocalised π-electrons and which undergo substitution rather than addition reactions. Compounds with normal single and double bonds are called *aliphatic* compounds.

Benzene undergoes addition reactions with hydrogen and chlorine. Hydrogen with a nickel catalyst (at 400 K and under pressure) converts benzene to cyclohexane:

When chlorine is activated by ultraviolet light, it adds to benzene, the chlorine atoms attacking the otherwise inert double bonds (cf. alkanes and chlorine, page 216):

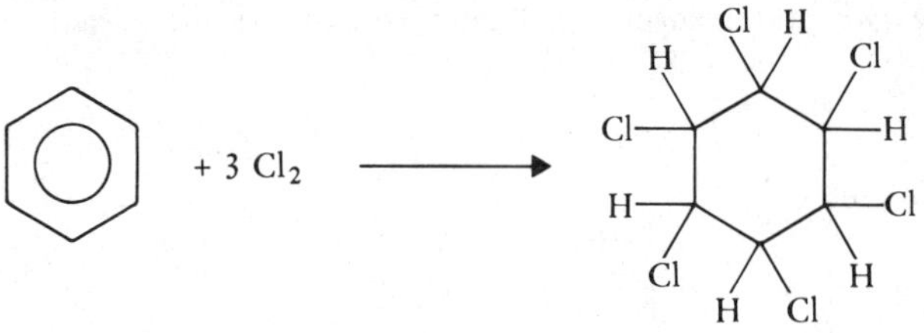

hexachlorocylcohexane

Make a model of the product — are there any conformers or isomers of your product? There are two conformers (see page 205) and several isomers — for example, all chlorine atoms could lie above the plane of the ring with the hydrogen atoms below it; the chlorine atoms in alternate positions could lie below the ring; etc. At least one of these isomers is a very effective insecticide.

Of more importance are the substitution reactions.

(a) Nitration of benzene

If benzene is warmed (below $50°C$ to prevent polysubstitution) with a mixture of concentrated nitric acid and concentrated sulphuric acid, the aromatic ring is attacked and hydrogen is displaced. The mixture of acids contains the nitronium ion, NO_2^+, which is attracted to the high electron density of the π-bond system:

$$2HNO_3 \rightleftharpoons H_2O + NO_2^+ + NO_3^-$$

(Sulphuric acid removes the water to shift the equilibrium to the right, in accordance with Le Chatelier's principle.)

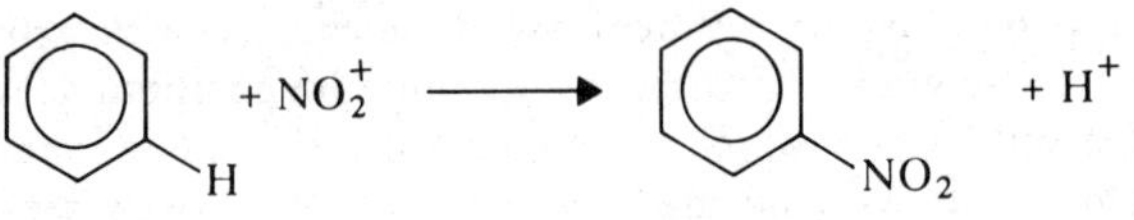

nitrobenzene

Nitro compounds are important compounds in the preparation of dyestuffs and explosives.

(b) Sulphonation of benzene

Benzene can be sulphonated by reaction with 'oleum' at $50°C$. Oleum is also known as fuming sulphuric acid or pyrosulphuric acid. It is concentrated sulphuric acid containing an excess of sulphur trioxide. The sulphonium ion attacks the benzene to give benzenesulphonic acid:

This is a useful reaction as sulphonation is used to prepare detergents.

(c) Halogenation of benzene

It was noted that, in the presence of ultraviolet light, benzene undergoes an addition reaction with halogenes. If, instead, a catalyst is used, then substitution occurs. The catalysts (often called halogen carriers) are Lewis acids (page 29) and polarise the halogen molecule aiding its attack on benzene. The usual catalysts are iron or iron(III) bromide:

bromobenzene

(d) Alkylation and acylation of benzene

The introduction of an alkyl group is described as *alkylation*. The formation of a ketone by the reaction of benzene and an acyl chloride is *acylation*. In the presence of anhydrous aluminium chloride as catalyst, alkyl and acyl chlorides (e.g. CH_3Cl and CH_3COCl respectively) attack benzene on heating:

methylbenzene   methylphenylketone
(or, toluene)   (or, acetophenone)

This reaction is known as the Friedel-Craft's reaction.

Alcohols

Alcohols have four possible reaction points — substitution at the bonds C—C, C—H, C—O, O—H. Of these, only the latter two are significant.

(a) Esterification of alcohols

When alcohols are reacted with acids, fruity-smelling products called *esters* are formed:

$$CH_3COOH + C_2H_5OH \rightleftharpoons CH_3COOC_2H_5 + H_2O$$
ethanoic   ethanol   ethyl ethanoate
acid

The esters are named as 'alkyl alkanoate' where the alkyl group is derived from the alcohol and the alkanoate is the acid grouping. This reaction is catalysed by mineral acids (e.g. hydrochloric acid, sulphuric acid) and goes to equilibrium. If water is removed, then, according to Le Chatelier's principle, the equilibrium will shift to offset this removal, so it moves to the right thereby increasing the yield of ester. The water can be removed by sulphuric acid (which also acts as the catalyst). Other techniques for the removal of water are available but this is the simplest method. As an alternative to the acid, ethanoyl chloride can be used:

$$CH_3COCl + C_2H_5OH \rightarrow CH_3COOC_2H_5 + HCl$$

This has the advantage that the hydrogen chloride is more easily displaced as a gas and so the reaction gives a higher yield of ester. An examination of the equation indicates that the hydrogen of the alcohol combines with the chlorine of the acid chloride. So, the O—H bond of the alcohol is broken. Similarly, in the reaction between the acid and alcohol, the C—O bond of the acid is broken and the OH group released reacts with the hydrogen of the alcohol:

$$CH_3CO \boxed{OH} + C_2H_5O \boxed{H}$$

(b) Halogenation of alcohols

Alcohols react with covalent chlorides to give halogenoalkanes. Hydrogen chloride is passed through a mixture of alcohol and anhydrous zinc chloride catalyst which is heated under reflux:

$$C_2H_5OH + HCl \rightarrow C_2H_5Cl + H_2O$$

A similar reaction is possible for hydrogen bromide, though it is usually performed with potassium bromide and concentrated sulphuric acid. The salt and acid generate hydrogen bromide and the acid also acts as a catalyst.

Alternatively, the phosphorus halides may be used. This method is particularly suitable for the iodide, which is generated by using red phosphorus and iodine:

$$2P + 3I_2 \rightarrow 2PI_3$$
$$3CH_3CH_2OH + PI_3 \rightarrow 3CH_3CH_2I + H_3PO_3$$
iodoethane

Phosphorus(V) chloride is normally used rather than the elements or phosphorus(III) chloride:

$$CH_3CH_2OH + PCl_5 \rightarrow CH_3CH_2Cl + POCl_3 + HCl$$

A very useful chlorinating agent is thionyl chloride, $SOCl_2$. This has the advantage that the secondary products are gases, and the excess thionyl chloride is volatile and so is easily removed:

$$C_3H_7OH + SOCl_2 \rightarrow C_3H_7Cl + SO_2 + HCl$$

This reaction involves the cleavage of the C—O bond of the alcohol.

(c) Dehydration of alcohols

If an alcohol is heated to 440 K with concentrated sulphuric acid water molecules are eliminated from the alcohol to give an alkene:

$$CH_3CH_2OH \xrightarrow{\text{conc. } H_2SO_4} CH_2=CH_2 + H_2O$$

The same product is obtained if the alcohol vapour is passed over an alumina catalyst at $350°C$. Concentrated sulphuric acid and alumina both have great affinities for water so aiding its removal from an alcohol.

(d) Oxidation of alcohols

While, in most reactions, alcohols can be considered merely as hydroxy groups attached to carbon backbones, it is useful to classify them into three groups for this reaction.

Primary alcohols are those in which the OH is attached to a carbon atom which has only *one* alkyl substituent, that is it is attached to a CH_2 group:

$$CH_3\underline{CH_2}OH$$

$$CH_3CH_2\underline{CH_2}OH$$

$$\begin{array}{c} CH_3 \\ | \\ CH_3-CH-\underline{CH_2}-OH \end{array}$$

When these are heated with permanganate or dichromate ions in acidic media, aldehydes are produced:

$$3CH_3CH_2OH + K_2Cr_2O_7 + 4H_2SO_4 \rightarrow 3CH_3CHO + Cr_2(SO_4)_3 + K_2SO_4 + 7H_2O$$
$$\text{ethanal}$$

Reaction with excess oxidising agent gives the acid:

$$3CH_3CHO + K_2Cr_2O_7 + 4H_2SO_4 \rightarrow 3CH_3COOH + 4H_2O + Cr_2(SO_4)_3 + K_2SO_4$$
$$\text{ethanoic acid}$$

Secondary alcohols have the hydroxy group attached to a carbon atom with two alkyl substituents (i.e. CH grouping):

$$\begin{array}{c} CH_3 \\ | \\ CH_3-\underline{CH}-OH \end{array}$$

(propan-2-ol)

These alcohols are oxidised to ketones:

$$3CH_3CH(OH)CH_3 + K_2Cr_2O_7 + 4H_2SO_4 \rightarrow 3CH_3COCH_3 + Cr_2(SO_4)_3 + K_2SO_4$$
propanone
(or, acetone)

$$+7H_2O$$

Further oxidation would necessitate cleavage of C—C bonds, and so can only occur in the presence of very strong oxidising agents such as concentrated nitric acid.

Tertiary alcohols involve hydroxyl groups attached to carbon atoms with three alkyl substituents and no hydrogen atoms:

$$
\begin{array}{c}
\quad CH_3 \\
\quad | \\
CH_3\!-\!C\!-\!OH \quad \text{2-methylpropan-2-ol} \\
\quad | \\
\quad CH_3
\end{array}
$$

These are stable to oxidation. In strongly acidic media they undergo elimination reactions instead. For example, 2-methylpropan-2-ol is converted to the alkene, 2-methylpropene

$$
\begin{array}{c}
\quad OH \\
\quad | \\
CH_3\!-\!C\!-\!CH_3 \xrightarrow{H^+} CH_3\!-\!C\!\!=\!\!CH_2 + H_2O \\
\quad | \qquad\qquad\qquad\quad | \\
\quad CH_3 \qquad\qquad\qquad CH_3
\end{array}
$$

which is oxidised to a ketone and carbon dioxide.

$$5(CH_3)_2C\!\!=\!\!CH_2 + 8Cr_2O_7^{2-} + 72H^+ \rightarrow 5(CH_3)_2CO + 5CO_2 + 16Cr^{3+} + 41H_2O$$
propanone

Phenols

Phenols are closely related to alcohols in that they involve hydroxy groups attached to a carbon skeleton. They differ in that the benzene ring affects the degree of reactivity of the OH group. The O—H bond is weaker but the C—O bond is stronger. In fact, the OH group cannot be cleaved from the ring to a significant extent. There is, for example, very little product on mixing a phenol with PCl_5. What would you expect to get?(See the corresponding reaction with alcohols.)

The weakness of the O—H bond is illustrated in the following two reactions.

(d) Acidic properties
The bond is broken by water to release a solvated hydrogen ion:

$$C_6H_5OH + H_2O \rightleftharpoons C_6H_5O^-(aq) + H_3O^+(aq)$$

Phenol is, therefore, a weak acid of $pK_a = 10.00$. As an acid, it reacts with sodium hydroxide solution to form a salt:

$$C_6H_5OH + NaOH \rightarrow C_6H_5O^-Na^+ + H_2O$$
$$\text{sodium phenate}$$

Alcohols, in contrast, are *not* acidic and do *not* react with sodium hydroxide; they will only react with very reactive metals such as sodium to display hydrogen.

(*b*) **Esterification**

Phenols and acids, or their derivatives, react to form esters in *alkaline* medium:

$$C_6H_5OH + CH_3COCl \rightarrow CH_3COOC_6H_5 + HCl$$

(c) **Aromatic properties**

Phenol possesses a benzene ring and so can undergo substitution reactions as for benzene. The OH group activates the ring and makes it more sensitive to attack than benzene. For example, bromination can be performed with bromine solution (rather than the more active liquid element) and no catalyst, and gives a trisubstituted compound rather than a monosubstituted product:

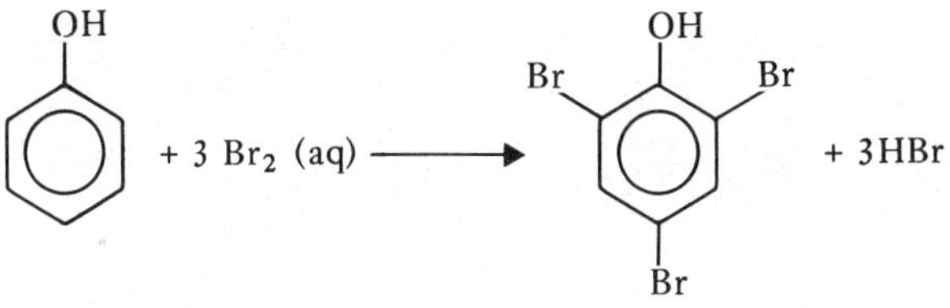

2, 4, 6-tribromophenol

Carbonyl compounds

There are two series of carbonyl compounds:
1. aldehydes – R.CHO, where R is a hydrocarbon group;
2. ketones – R.CO.R', where R and R' are hydrocarbon groupings.
Each of these compounds contains the carbonyl group

$$\text{\textbackslash} \atop C=O \atop \text{/}$$

Since there is a double bond between the carbon and the oxygen atoms, the typical reactions are addition reactions.

(*a*) **Addition reactions**
Polar compounds add to the carbonyl group:

(i) *Reaction with hydrogen cyanide*

$$\overset{\delta+}{\underset{/}{\diagdown}} \overset{\delta-}{C} = O + \overset{\delta+}{H} - \overset{\delta-}{CN} \rightarrow \underset{\underset{CN}{|}}{\overset{|}{-C}} - OH$$

For example, with ethanal:

$$CH_3CHO + HCN \rightarrow CH_3CH(OH)CN$$
2-hydroxypropanenitrile

(ii) *Reaction with ammonia*

Aliphatic aldehydes react with ammonia:

$$\underset{/}{\diagdown}C = O + NH_3 \rightarrow \underset{\underset{OH}{|}}{\overset{|}{-C}} - NH_2$$

Ketones and aromatic aldehydes do not react in this manner; their reaction is more complex. With ethanal, the product is 1-aminoethanol.

(iii) *Reaction with sodium hydrogen sulphite*

Aldehydes and ketones react with sodium hydrogen sulphite to give an addition compound:

$$CH_3 \cdot \overset{\overset{O}{\|}}{C} \cdot CH_3 + Na^+HSO_3^- \rightarrow CH_3 \cdot \underset{\underset{SO_3^-Na^+}{|}}{\overset{\overset{OH}{|}}{C}} \cdot CH_3$$

sodium 2-hydroxypropanesulphonate

(*b*) **Condensation reactions**

Carbonyl compounds react with substituted ammonia compounds to form the imino grouping

$$\underset{/}{\diagdown}C = N -$$

together with the elimination of water. The basic reaction is

$$R \cdot CO \cdot R' + H_2N \cdot Y \rightarrow \underset{R'}{\overset{R}{\diagdown}} C = N \cdot Y + H_2O$$

With hydroxyammonia (or hydroxylamine), an *oxime* is produced:

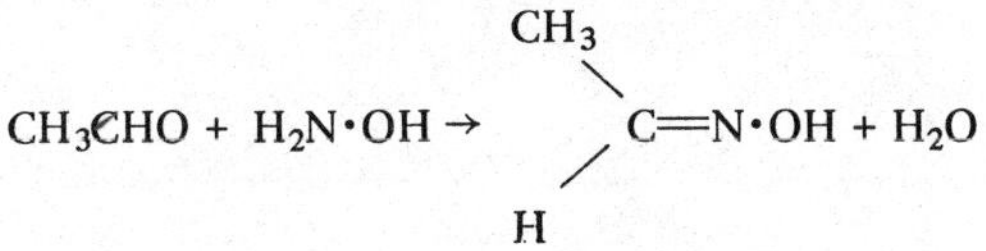

$$CH_3CHO + H_2N \cdot OH \rightarrow \overset{CH_3}{\underset{H}{>}} C{=}N \cdot OH + H_2O$$

ethanal oxime

Hydrazine reacts with carbonyl compounds to form *hydrazones*, or, with an excess of the carbonyl compound, *azines*:

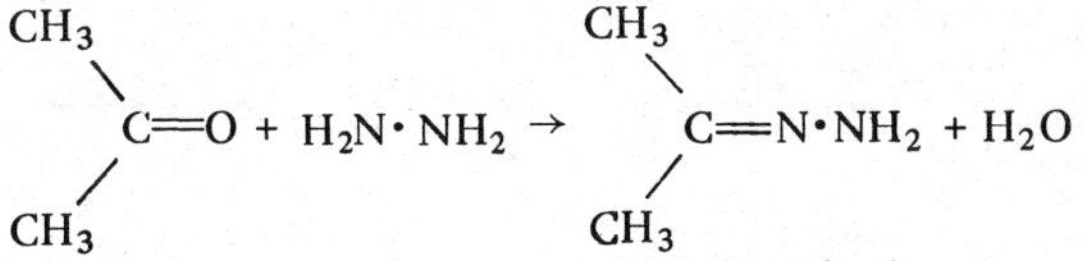

$$\overset{CH_3}{\underset{CH_3}{>}} C{=}O + H_2N \cdot NH_2 \rightarrow \overset{CH_3}{\underset{CH_3}{>}} C{=}N \cdot NH_2 + H_2O$$

propanone hydrazone

$$\overset{CH_3}{\underset{CH_3}{>}} C{=}N \cdot NH_2 + O{=}C \overset{CH_3}{\underset{CH_3}{<}} \rightarrow \overset{CH_3}{\underset{CH_3}{>}} C{=}N{-}N{=}C \overset{CH_3}{\underset{CH_3}{<}} + H_2O$$

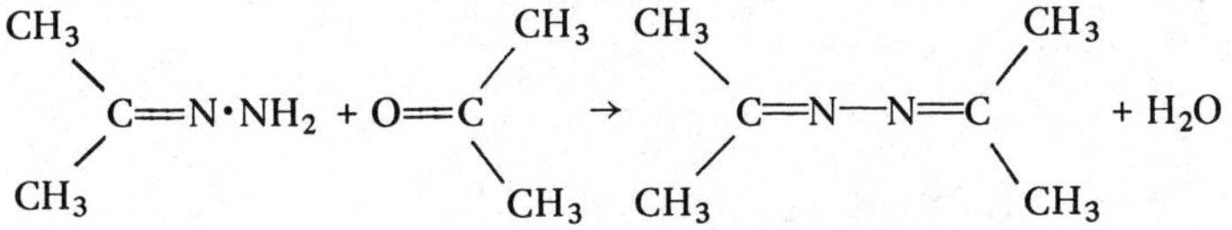

propanone azine

Several substituted hydrazines can also be used. For example, phenylhydrazine, $C_6H_5NH \cdot NH_2$ give *phenylhydrazones*. A useful derivative of this reagent is 2,4-dinitrophenylhydrazine, known as Brady's reagent. The 2,4-dinitrophenylhydrazones are highly crystalline yellow or orange derivatives:

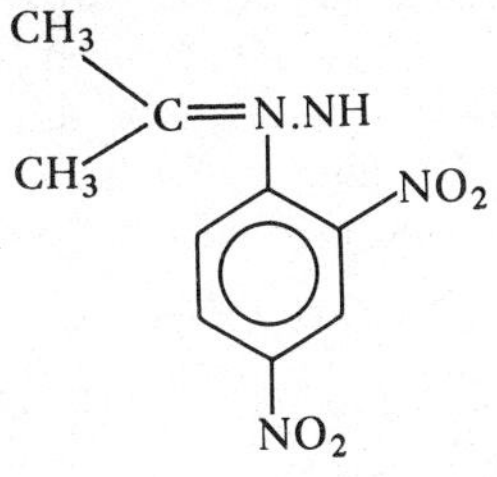

Semicarbazide, in the presence of sodium ethanoate, condenses with carbonyl compounds to give colourless crystals of a *semicarbazone*:

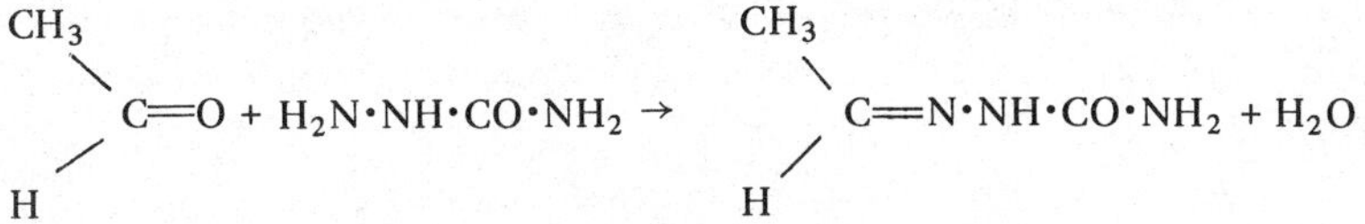

$$\overset{CH_3}{\underset{H}{>}} C{=}O + H_2N \cdot NH \cdot CO \cdot NH_2 \rightarrow \overset{CH_3}{\underset{H}{>}} C{=}N \cdot NH \cdot CO \cdot NH_2 + H_2O$$

Amines also react with carbonyl compounds to form *anils*, or Schiff bases. At least one of the hydrocarbon groups must be aromatic to stabilise the anil:

$$R \cdot CO \cdot R' + R''NH_2 \rightarrow \begin{array}{c} R \\ \diagdown \\ \diagup \\ R' \end{array} C=N \cdot R'' + H_2O$$

(c) Oxidation of carbonyls

Aldehydes and ketones differ in their ease of oxidation. Aldehydes are readily oxidised to the corresponding acids:

$$C_6H_5 \cdot CHO \xrightarrow[H^+]{K_2Cr_2O_7} C_6H_5 \cdot COOH$$

Ketones, in contrast, can only be oxidised by strong oxidising agents. Hot, acidic potassium permanganate solution causes cleavage of a C—C bond in ketones to give a mixture of acids:

$$\begin{array}{c} CH_3 \\ \diagdown \\ \diagup \\ C_3H_7 \end{array} C=O \xrightarrow[H^+]{KMnO_4} CH_3COOH + C_2H_5COOH$$

Yields are usually poor for ketones.

The difference in oxidisability of these compounds is the basis of some simple distinctive tests for aldehydes. Aldehydes are able to reduce alkaline solutions of some metal salts to the lower oxide or metal. For example, an ammoniacal solution of silver nitrate is reduced by an aldehyde to silver. If the reaction is performed in a clean test-tube and the reduction is allowed to proceed slowly, the silver becomes deposited on the glass giving a silver mirror. The reagent is known as Tollen's reagent. This reagent can be

$$CH_3CHO + 2Ag(NH_3)_2OH \rightarrow CH_3COONH_4 + 2Ag + H_2O + NH_3(aq)$$

hazardous and should not be stored. The reaction product should be washed away immediately after use.

Copper(II) salts can be used for a similar test; they are reduced to red copper(I) oxide. Unfortunately copper(II) salts are not soluble in alkaline solution and so a complexing agent is used. Fehling's solution is prepared in two parts: 'A' is copper(II) sulphate solution and 'B' is sodium potassium tartarate in sodium hydroxide solution. When these are mixed in the presence of an aldehyde and warmed, a red precipitate of the copper(I) oxide is formed.

$$CH_3CHO + 2Cu^{2+} + Na^+OH^- + H_2O \rightarrow CH_3COONa + Cu_2O + 4H^+$$

Other complexing agents can be used at different pH's:

   copper ethanoate in ethanoic acid (Barfoed's reagent);
   copper citrate in sodium carbonate (Benedict's solution);
   copper tartarate in sodium hydroxide and excess ammonia (Pavy).

Perhaps the easiest variation, because the solution is stable as a mixture over an indefinite period is the copper(II)—EDTA complex in sodium hydroxide (EDTA is a powerful complexing agent).

Acids

Carboxylic acids contain the group

$$-C \overset{\displaystyle O}{\underset{\displaystyle OH}{\big\backslash}}$$

. This group is planar. As seen in Table 15.4, the acids are named by adding the suffix 'oic acid' to the stem. For example, H·COOH is one carbon acid and so is named methanoic acid. (It has previously been popularly named formic acid.) CH_3COOH is ethanoic acid (also known as acetic acid). The melting points of these acids follow an irregular pattern (Table 16.3), though the boiling points show the expected trend. This difference is related to the formation of hydrogen-bonding. The acids tend to form dimers — i.e. two basic units combined.

$$CH_3-C \overset{\displaystyle O\cdots H-O}{\underset{\displaystyle O-H\cdots O}{}} C-CH_3$$

Ethanoic acid tends to freeze on a cold day (below 290 K) and so is often called glacial ethanoic acid, in contrast to the aqueous solution which has a significantly lower melting point.

Table 16.3 Physical properties of carboxylic acids

Formula	M.p./K	B.p./K	pK_a
HCOOH	281	374	3.75
CH_3COOH	290	391	4.76
CH_3CH_2COOH	252	414	4.87
$CH_3CH_2CH_2COOH$	269	437	4.82
C_6H_5COOH	395	522	4.20
$C_6H_5CH_2COOH$	249	539	4.31

(a) Acidic properties

The acids are soluble in water forming weakly acidic solutions (see page 178):

$$CH_3COOH(aq) \rightarrow CH_3COO^-(aq) + H^+(aq)$$

As an acid, ethanoic acid undergoes the normal neutralisation reactions with alkali (NaOH, Na_2CO_3) and metals (Mg).

(b) Reactions of the OH group

The acidic properties involve the breakage of the O—H bond (compare phenols). But it is also possible to break the C—O bond as in alcohols. For example, the carboxylic acids react with covalent chlorides to evolve hydrogen chloride gas (a test for the presence of OH groups):

$CH_3CH_2COOH + PCl_5 \rightarrow CH_3CH_2COCl + POCl_3 + HCl(g)$
propanoic acid   propanoyl chloride

With alcohols, acids form esters by cleavage of the C—O bond in acids (see page 222):

$CH_3CH_2COOH + CH_3OH \rightarrow CH_3CH_2COOCH_3 + H_2O$
                           methyl propanoate

Carboxylic acids are sometimes known as 'fatty acids' since the higher homologues are formed by the hydrolysis of fats — e.g. fats formed by the esterification of glycerol ($HOCH_2 \cdot CH(OH) \cdot CH_2OH$) and palmitic acid (heptadecanoic acid, $CH_3(CH_2)_{14}COOH$), stearic acid (octadecanoic acid, $CH_3(CH_2)_{16}COOH$) or oleic acid (octadec-9-enoic acid, $CH_3(CH_2)_7CH = CH(CH_2)_7COOH$).

Amines

Amines are the organic bases. They contain the grouping —NH_2 (see Table 16.4). These are primary amines — that is compounds with one hydrocarbon group attached to the amino group. Secondary amines involve two carbon groups on the nitrogen:

		pK_b
$(CH_3)_2NH$	N-methylaminomethane or dimethylamine	3.28
$(C_2H_5)_2NH$	N-ethylaminoethane or diethylamine	3.02

and tertiary amines have three carbon groups on the nitrogen:

$(CH_3)_3N$ N,N-dimethylaminomethane or trimethylamine $pK_b = 4.31$

(The prefix N in some of the names is added to indicate that the substituent is placed on the nitrogen atom rather than the carbon chain).

Basic character

It will be observed that, with the exception of aniline, all of the amines are stronger than ammonia (pK_b 4.75). In general, the base strength increases with the degree of substitution by alkyl groups. Amines react with water to form basic solutions:

$CH_3NH_2 + H_2O \rightleftharpoons CH_3\overset{+}{N}H_3 + OH^-$

and with acids to form salts:

$C_2H_5NH_2 + HCl \rightarrow C_2H_5NH_3^+ + Cl^-$
                 ethylammonium chloride

Table 16.4 Some primary amines and their strengths   231

Formula	Name	pK$_b$
CH_3NH_2	aminomethane or methylamine	3.36
$CH_3CH_2NH_2$	aminoethane or ethylamine	3.27
$CH_3CH_2CH_2NH_2$	1-aminopropane or propylamine	3.33
$CH_3.CH.CH_3$ $\quad\vert$ $\quad NH_2$	2-aminopropane	3.28
$C_6H_5NH_2$	aminobenzene, phenylamine or aniline	9.38

$$(CH_3)_2NH + HCl \rightarrow (CH_3)_2NH_2^+ + Cl^-$$
$$\text{dimethylammonium chloride}$$

They also react with halogenoalkanes to form tertiary substituted ammonium salts:

$$(CH_3)_3N + C_2H_5Cl \rightarrow (CH_3)_3NC_2H_5^+ + Cl^-$$
$$\text{ethyltrimethylammonium chloride}$$

With a base strength greater than that of ammonia, it would be expected that they would form strong complexes with metals in a manner similar to ammonia:

$$[Cu(H_2O)_4]^{2+} + 4RNH_2 \rightarrow [Cu(RNH_2)_4]^{2+} + 4H_2O$$

With amines having large alkyl groups the stability may be less than expected from the base strength due to steric hindrance (that is bulky groups get in the way of each other).

Aniline is a weaker base because of the non-bonding electron pair on the nitrogen, which is responsible for basic character and is less readily available (it is involved in strengthening the bonds between the nitrogen and the ring). A similar feature arises with phenols and their complexing ability; they have a weaker coordinating ability than alcohols.

Summary

At the conclusion of this chapter, you should be able to:

1. describe the combustion of organic compounds;
2. name the different reducing agents available for the reduction of organic compounds;
3. give examples of substitution reactions of alkenes;
4. describe the addition reactions of ethene;

5. state and apply Markovnikov's rule;
6. describe the difference between benzene and alkenes;
7. describe the addition reactions of hydrogen and chlorine with benzene;
8. give examples of the substitution reactions of benzene;
9. describe the esterification, halogenation, dehydration and oxidation reactions of alcohols;
10. describe the differences between alcohols and phenols;
11. give examples of the addition reactions of carbonyl compounds;
12. describe the condensation reactions of carbonyl derivatives with substituted ammonia compounds;
13. describe the oxidation of carbonyl compounds;
14. describe the typical properties of organic acids and bases.

Experiments

1. Reactions of the functional groups (e.g. *Nuffield, Advanced Science, Chemistry;* (Longman, 1970) topics 9 and 13).
2. Organic preparations (*Selected Experiments in Physical Science;* D. H. Marrow (Longman, 1974), Chapter 10).
3. Purifications of prepared compounds and tests for purity − e.g. phenyl benzoate, acetanilide.

References

Aromaticity; T. J. Harrington, *Sch. Sci. Rev.,* 1962, **43**, 361−73.

Questions

1. How do the following compounds react with hydrogen bromide: (*a*) ethene; (*b*) propene; (*c*) ethanol; (*d*) ethanamine?
2. Describe the reactions between bromine and (*a*) ethane; (*b*) hex-1-ene; (*c*) benzene; (*d*) phenol.
3. What are the products of the reaction between ethanoyl chloride and (*a*) benzene and (*b*) ethanol?
4. How does sulphuric acid react with (*a*) but-1-ene; (*b*) benzene; (*c*) propan-1-ol; (*d*) propanamine?
5. How would you prepare:
   (*a*) 2-bromoethanol from ethanol in two steps;
   (*b*) propan-2-ol from propan-1-ol in three steps;
   (*c*) ethyl ethanoate from ethanol as the only available organic reagent;
   (*d*) 2-aminopropan-2-ol from propan-2-ol in two steps.
6. How do methanamine and methanal each react with copper(II) sulphate?
7. What is the product of the reaction of potassium permanganate with (*a*) ethene; (*b*) propanal; (*c*) propan-1-ol?